Healer's Heart

Healer's Heart

A Family Physician's Stories of the Heart and Art of Medicine

by

Pamela Camosy

Published by Pamela Camosy
www.facebook.com/healersheartbook

Edited by Lillie Ammann
Cover design by Aundrea Hernandez
Interior design by Jan McClintock

ISBN:
Print: 978-0-692-94328-1
Ebook: 978-0-692-94329-8

DEDICATION

To my husband, Dennis, for your support, humor, and perspective. You show me every day that together we can make the world a better place.

To our beautiful daughters, Ann Marie and Caroline, for your encouragement throughout this project. You are the most compassionate people I know and a constant source of positive energy.

To my parents. Mom was my first role model for healing, tending to her own children and those of the neighborhood, as well as injured birds and other wild creatures. Dad taught me that hard work and honesty lead to great things.

TABLE OF CONTENTS

INTRODUCTION

The crisp autumn air is beginning to stir with activity on the street as I unlock the glass door and make my way inside. Amber rays of morning sunlight enter the dark room ahead of me, revealing shadowy outlines of neatly lined chairs, looking as if they already have patients in them.

As I walk through the waiting room, my mind whirs with a cloud of thoughts. *It was nice to see Mr. Martinez again yesterday. I wonder how his ankle is doing. Will we get our new stock of flu shots today? I don't want my elderly patients to start the winter season without it. I should remember to call Lori today; it has been almost a week since she returned home after a suicide attempt.*

My desk chair feels comfortable as I settle into it. I empty my briefcase of last night's paperwork and today's snacks and turn on my computer. Like most physicians, I frequently wish I did not have to spend so much time sitting in front of this shimmering square box, typing, correcting, clicking out my patient notes and medication orders.

Then the yang to this yin graciously reminds me, as I pour my first cup of coffee on this new day, to remember the joy.

Joy. When I tell medical students that I truly enjoy family medicine now as much as I did thirty years ago, they are surprised and pleased, being nascent doctors themselves. Several have told me that other physicians with whom they have worked expressed intense dissatisfaction with their present-day medical practice and the uncertain state of healthcare in America. Some doctors are leaving the profession at a much earlier age than they had planned when they set out as idealistic young medical students years ago. We speculate together that these professionals may have lost their sense of joy, which, in some sense, is understandable.

American medicine has been changing at a breathtaking pace, and there are even more unknowns coming our way as the new millennium continues to unfold. Conglomerate hospital systems, health insurance companies, and the federal government have wrested control of medical practice from individual physicians in a power transfer that created the "healthcare industry." New regulations require that I see more patients in less time. "Metrics" monitor how many of my diabetic and hypertensive patients are under control and what percentage of my patients has received their annual flu shot. The length of time that each of my patients stays in the hospital is closely monitored, with financial penalties levied for lengthy hospitalizations or return to the hospital within a certain period of time.

When I started out, I was a "doctor," but now I am a "healthcare provider" to the insurance companies. Is it any surprise, then, that physicians feel excluded from many of the important tasks of managing their patients? Or that patients lament having less-personal relationships with their physicians?

My joy is rooted in the realization that the focal point of my life as a doctor does not lie in these external, albeit inevitable, forces. The focus lies within me, it is totally within my control, and it is what gets me out of bed every morning: it is my ability to connect compassionately with my patients. The unfolding of my career as a family physician—from student to resident to experienced physician to *very* experienced physician—has shown me that my relationships with my patients carry a potent energy that is both healing for my patient and energizing for me.

Over the same span of years, I have come to view my medical school education as a gift, a surprising one to a shy and financially poor young woman who was the first in her large family to attend college. This gift must be treasured and compassionately shared with others. So, on this early morning as I sit alone in my office, before the staff arrives and before our patients begin to check in, I remind myself to stay joy-full, peace-full, and, above all, to cherish my time with patients. They entrust me with so much of themselves that I cannot help but feel honored. Within the sanctuary of my clinic or the hospital room, my patients bring me their pain, their problems, their heartaches. They also share their joys, successes, life lessons, and insights. Some tell me secrets that they have not told another soul on this earth. My patients teach me, they motivate me, and sometimes they heal me. In return, they are asking for my compassion, brainpower, and experience. Which of us is really giving more? Surely it is not me.

As I sip on my coffee and log onto my computer, my clinic staff members trickle in, and we begin our morning ritual of saying hello and getting ready for a busy day. My nurse and I look at today's schedule together to discuss briefly each patient on the list. Mr. Porter is coming in for his back pain again; we remember that he and his wife are divorcing. Little Katie Foster was in the hospital last week for pneumonia; this will be her one-week follow-up. We have Mr. Morris down for a blood pressure follow-up at two, but he is often a no-show. This might work out well today, because Mrs. Smith at 1:30 usually has many more complaints than she tells my secretary when she calls. We scan through the schedule to remind ourselves that this is not simply an appointment list, but a group of people who are seeking our help. Again, joy.

My nurse and I know that caring for our patients is as much an art as it is a science. Years of family practice and life in general have taught me that quality medical care does not emanate from the diplomas on my office wall; these are merely symbols of my medical knowledge. Quality medicine likewise is not a result of the stethoscope in my pocket or any technological device that I can summon. Certainly, these components are necessary for me to practice medicine well, but they are not sufficient. True healing flows from the positive energy of our relationship: I want each patient to feel as cared *about* as they are cared for.

Over the decades of my career, the patient interactions that I so cherish have survived the man-made creations of technology. These tools have been welcomed by physicians: CT scans and MRIs, automated lab analysis, robotic surgery, and yes, computerized medical records. Over the same span of years, I have learned how to deal with the requirements of healthcare corporations while preserving my patient relationships and my own professional joy.

Now, the American medical landscape is being transformed once again by thousands of unseen hands belonging to politicians. Our elected officials are trying to devise a new, more equitable system of medical care. As I read about the various legislative proposals, the more uncertain the image of medicine appears. I return to my primary professional defense mechanism: no one can touch my ability to connect compassionately with each and every patient I see. I will keep my joy.

If we carry this coping skill a step further, then everyone, every single one of us, can use our skills and talents in a positive way, no matter what the world throws our way. We can all be healers.

After my father died a few years ago, I was devastated. Dad had been a solid force in my life, as certain a presence as the sun that rose each morning. Daily life went on around me, though, and a few days later, I found myself in a department store shopping for a black dress. The only memory I have of that afternoon is a kind-faced store employee with a thick Russian accent.

"You sit here, dear," she said, patting the bench in the fitting room, "and I vill take care uf you."

She brought me dress after dress until we found the right one. After spending hours tending to my father on his death bed, I was being cared for by this salesclerk. In her soft gentle way, she was a healer to me.

So, even the roles of the healer and the hurting are not immutable. Within the patient-physician relationship, energy and emotions flow in both directions. You will read of the parents who lost their baby to sudden infant death syndrome, yet still had enough room in their hearts to help me in my feelings of inadequacy. Of a military veteran who helped me feel closer to my father after his death by telling me details about Vietnam that Dad himself never discussed. Of the patient who came to the clinic for high blood pressure and returned a while later with homemade baked goods to brighten my hectic day.

I put on my white lab coat, tuck my stethoscope into the pocket, and enter the exam room to greet my first patient. During several decades as a family physician, I have cared for thousands of people, and somewhere during the years I realized that many of my patient encounters were still alive in my memory, begging me to write them down. These patient experiences touched me in their humanity, their sense of amazement, and, yes, their joy. Some of the events are sad, some uplifting, some ordinary, but I must honor them as best I can, so that they do not escape unnoticed in perpetuity.

As you read *Healer's Heart*, you may relate to the patients whose paths have crossed mine. You have sat on a clinic exam table or lain in a hospital bed with your physician standing at your side. Perhaps you will recognize some of your own medical experiences and be reminded of a time when you were ill, very ill, perhaps even scary ill. You hoped that this new doctor you were about to see would really listen and care, not just go through the motions and then rush on to their next patient. You did not put a name to it then, but you were hoping for the positive energy of a "therapeutic relationship" with your doctor.

My hope, dear reader, is that you will gain an enhanced understanding of the process of developing therapeutic relationships, at least from my perspective. Join me as I take you from the difficult, yet rewarding, days of the medical school lecture hall and cadaver lab, to a family practice residency training that consisted of the time-honored "see-one-do-one-teach-one" rubric, and then down the hospital and clinic corridors with me as your physician guide. Throughout this journey, you will witness a healer grow in experience, knowledge, and humility, even as a medical care system explodes with technological advances and financial convolutions.

Consider as you read that the art of medicine, the heart of medicine, is deserving of our celebration.

Note: I have changed all names to protect the confidentiality of my patients and coworkers. In some cases, I have altered the gender, location, or other identifying characteristics or combined separate patient stories into one.

1

PASSAGES

My God, she looks small.

She is a frail, thin bundle within the white hospital sheets, tiny eyes closed in her age-worn wrinkled skin. Her face is familiar, yet somehow different. She is thinner after her rapid weight loss and her face paler from severe blood loss. Her sweetness remains, however. As I stand at the doorway, my mind flashes back to her visits to my clinic over the years—her smiles, her soft pats to my hands, her gifts of homemade brownies.

And, oh, yes, her lessons. Mrs. Feller is a genteel Charleston belle with an accent to match. When we first met, I was enchanted by the lyrical sound of every sentence she spoke, and I told her as much.

With unassuming grace, she told me, "I was bone hee-yah, doc-tah." And then she taught me to say, "Isn't Chahl-ston a gaw-geous place to lay-iv?"

I step into her hospital room. Dark pink azaleas, now in full bloom in all of South Carolina, rest in a glass vase on the windowsill, not far from an IV pole. The clear fluid silently enters her veins as I ease myself into the chair next to her bed, glad to be off my feet. My happiness is minuscule, of course, next to the weight of her medical prognosis. She is dying.

Last year, at just sixty-four years old, she came to me complaining of fatigue.

"I can't tend to my roses any more, Dr. Camosy," she said, truly saddened.

I discovered that she had abdominal tenderness and iron-deficiency anemia; put together these were worrisome signs of colon cancer. Exploratory surgery confirmed the diagnosis, but the cancer was much too widespread for the surgeons to remove. For the next year or so, the cancer in her abdomen continued to grow and to bleed. From time to precious time, when she grew too tired to carry on, she came to my clinic to be admitted to the hospital for a blood transfusion.

Mrs. Feller and her husband, a childless couple, set their affairs in order, and together they achieved a sort of peace with her prognosis. But the cancer took its toll in short order. Her weight dropped forty pounds; her strength rapidly waned. Eventually she told me that she did not want any more transfusions. Now she lies in our hospital, and I am honored to care for her during her last days.

Mrs. Feller opens her eyes when I sit down, and her weak smile is a gift in my busy day. I have seen a stronger version of that smile many times in my clinic.

"How are they doing?" she asks me, as I take her frail hand in mine.

"The mom is six centimeters dilated, and her baby is doing well," I tell her. "Her labor is going smoothly and rapidly."

That very same day, down on the fifth-floor labor and delivery ward, I am following a patient who is in labor with her first child. Anna Gentry presented just a few hours ago in active labor and more than a little anxious. I did a pelvic exam and applied a tiny fetal monitor to the baby's scalp as the nurse strapped the ultrasound belt to the mother's abdomen. A few minutes of my watching the dual tracings allowed me to reassure Mom and Dad that all indicators were reassuring.

In between contractions, she and her husband told me of their excitement to be finally having the baby. They described the freshly painted nursery and a new rocking chair, a gift from his parents.

The labor ward is bustling today, noisy and full of activity. The mood is hectic yet upbeat as the nurses and doctors go about their duties. Unspoken in everyone's mind is the prospect of new life entering our world. Their job—my job—is to keep mom and baby healthy during the arduous process.

The hospital elevator carries me up and down between the fifth and ninth floors as I care for my two patients. Hours pass, and Mrs. Feller grows predictably weaker. I adjust the IV morphine drip as best I can to keep her comfortable without ending her respirations completely, which is a delicate balancing act. She becomes increasingly interested in how Anna is doing and asks me each time I enter her room if the baby has been born yet. I should not be surprised. My intuition tells me that for her, *this* baby entering the world on *this* day will be a fitting and providential counterbalance to her leaving it.

As the elevator carries me back down, the link between my two patients becomes impossible to ignore. My doctor-calculations of drug dosages, electrolytes, and fetal monitor variability give way to contemplation. I feel in the soulful part of me that an unseen hand is weaving me into the timeless cycle of life that sustains all that we know. I say a quick prayer, asking God for a peace-filled, painless death for Mrs. Feller and for a healthy birth for Anna and her baby. Then I present Him with an audacious request: that Anna will give birth before Mrs. Feller dies.

As the next few hours unfold, baby Jonathan is born, wrinkly and red and screaming lustily. As I lay him on his mother's chest for their first hello, I touch one of his pink palms, and his tiny hand wraps around my finger. This is just a palmar grasp reflex, I am fully aware, but it is a rewarding sensation nonetheless.

"Hi there, little tweedy-pie," his father murmurs, planting a gentle kiss on the baby's cheek.

A while later the elevator brings me upward again, and on this ride in my "chapel of St. Otis," I pray for myself, for the skills and compassion to fulfill my role in God's plan for life's passages. And I pray that Mrs. Feller is still alive.

When I enter her room, her husband is sitting at the bedside, his forehead bent down and resting on the mattress. Her eyes are barely open, but they turn toward me as I enter the room.

"A healthy baby boy," I respond to the question her eyes are asking me. "Mother and baby are doing well, and the new father is on a cloud!"

She settles back into the bed, her life and her pain almost at their end. She can no longer speak, so I sit wordlessly with her and hold her weak, cool hand. Her husband sits across from me, caressing the other. I see in her face a sense of peace, and when she dies a few hours later, drifting out of our world and into another, I feel it, too.

2

TOOTIE

Becoming a physician is not for the faint of heart.

My first patient interview took place at the open ward of the military hospital near our medical school. *My mind is blank—what do I ask him? He must be thinking that I am an idiot.* My first physical examination. *Should I use the bell or the diaphragm side of my stethoscope? Are my cheeks turning red?* My first spinal tap. *What if I go too far with the needle and paralyze my patient?* My first liver biopsy—first suicidal patient— first cardiac arrest.

Long before all these uncomfortable moments, however, even before I ever see my first patient, comes first-year gross anatomy class. "Gross," we medical students call it—not the adjective but the noun, as in "we have gross this afternoon." As I try to prepare for our first session by reviewing the written class manual, all I can think is, *Will I faint when I see the cadavers?*

On the first day of gross anatomy class, our instructor, a distinguished-looking man who held a PhD in anatomy, meets us in the lecture hall. He gives us an introduction to the class, which would span most of our first year. We are about to start the most important class of our med school career, he tells us. Most professors tell us this, but for some reason we really believe it today. A brief history of human dissection follows. Early medical scientists and physicians, we learn, had to resort to clandestine grave-robbing in the name of advancing the quality of medical care to living patients.

The professor's voice then turns quieter. In a solemn tone, he tells us of the immense privilege that lies just ahead for us student doctors. Very few people on the face of the earth are allowed to do what we are about to do—dissect a human body. We must always remember that each body lying downstairs in the anatomy lab was once a human being, who lived and worked and played among other human beings. Because they decided to leave their body to medical science, we can learn from it and become better healers. He concludes by reminding us that we must always maintain a respectful attitude in the lab. Our heads nod in quiet assent. The respect part is easy to understand, but my main thought at that moment is still, *Will I faint when I see the cadavers?*

As we change into green hospital scrubs in the restroom near the lecture hall, no one speaks. The air feels thick. We take the elevator down to the basement and then make our way through long, unfamiliar hallways. Monotone beige-tiled walls and floors bid us continue until we reach a set of double doors marked "Gross Anatomy Lab." Under that sign are two more: a yellow "Authorized Personnel Only" sign and a second with a red and black biohazard symbol. I get the message, both of them, as I don surgical gloves with the rest of my classmates. My heart is pounding.

Mine is the second group of four med students to enter the lab. I step inside with my three tank mates—there was a new term for us all. *Will I faint?* Immediately an acrid odor fills my nostrils and burns my eyes, and I take in the surreal scene. Several dozen metal casket-esque boxes, about three feet above the floor, are spaced evenly across the huge room. Atop each is a cloth-draped and eerily familiar form on a wire meshed pallet. *No, not dizzy yet.* The lab assistant (the deaner, another new word) leads the four of us to our station, and the potent smell grows exponentially. I soon see why. Each tank contains gallons and gallons of clear yellow formaldehyde, enough to cover the body when lowered back down at the end of each day.

My eyes quickly flicker back up to the draped form as John, the boldest of us all at that moment, reaches across to uncover the cadaver's head and shoulders. *And I'm still standing.* It is—she is—an old woman, with tan-grey wrinkly skin covering an emaciated frame.

The rest of us take John's lead. As we uncover her waxy extremities, I am filled with a sense of disbelief that one human could actually be doing this to another. My gloved fingers touch her stiff bony knees and then her gnarled feet. I look back over to her face, and realize that, with a little imagination, one could think that she was merely asleep.

"She looks like she's sleeping."

Another tank mate echoes my thought, and from then on, we refer to the cadaver as "she" and not "it." One of us suggests that we give her a name.

"Would that be disrespectful?" someone asks. "She had her own name, after all."

"I think it would be just the opposite," answers the deaner, who is passing by.

He stays for a moment to show us the surgical instruments we will be using. He has lined them precisely atop a green surgical drape on a Mayo-stand off to the side of the cadaver: scalpel, blunt and sharp probes, and forceps. He swings the stand around so that its top is directly over *her* abdomen. The instruments are now easy for us to see and to use.

Today we do no cutting, however. The professor addresses the group when everyone has found their cadavers. He explains the basics of the surgical instruments for probing, blunt dissection, and sharp dissection. He gives us a review of basic anatomical directional words to help us understand the instructions in our workbook: cephalad/caudad, dorsal/ventral, medial/lateral. As he speaks, we explore the cadaver tentatively, touching and poking, moving her arms and legs. My scientific curiosity begins to overcome my trepidation.

"Tootie," someone in our group says softly. "We should call her Tootie."

So, Tootie it is. I am still upright and feeling fine, sporting a tremendous sense of personal accomplishment, as we finish our first day in gross.

When we next enter the lab, each cadaver has been turned onto its abdomen. This allows us to dissect the back muscles, the latissimus dorsi, which are among the largest muscles in the body. The "lats" are an appropriate target for our inexperienced hands. We notice three round eaten-away lesions, each about an inch in diameter, on Tootie's tailbone and pelvic bone prominences. It is my first look at bedsores. We deduce that she most likely had been a nursing home patient, immobilized by infirmity of some sort, and may even have died there.

Tootie, God love her, serves me and my tank mates well for the next eight months. We pore over the step-by-step instructions in the workbook and wield the surgical instruments looking for structures like eager pirates in search of buried treasure. Our four heads bend down intently for hours on end, as we dissect, poke, and search.

"There it is!" we exclaim, often in unison, as we painstakingly isolate and identify some spindly, thread-like nerve.

We learn from our lung dissection that Tootie was a smoker. Her lung tissue is coarsely blackened compared to the smooth pale tissue of the cadavers on either side of us.

As the weeks progress, we cut into every part of her body, carefully searching for muscles, nerves, arteries, and veins. We marvel at her heart valves and her renal calyces, and we discover that she had a hysterectomy. In her brain's basilar artery, we come upon a calcified blood clot, which we know would have totally occluded the blood flow when she was alive. Our anatomy instructor invites the other students to look at this finding, and it is not hard for us to deduce that she likely died from a massive brainstem stroke. Tootie's family may or may not have known what killed her, but we now do. I go home that day exhausted and reeking of formaldehyde until after a long, hot shower, but with a definite intellectual satisfaction.

My positive attitude lasts only until our first gross anatomy test. After each teaching unit, the professor choses one or two cadavers for the test, marking them with cardboard letters and arrows: A→, B→ and so on. We students revolve around each cadaver with our test papers and are required to identify each structure by name. On that day, the structures look so tiny and nondescript that I am literally shaking with anxiety. When I studied them in our *Gray's Anatomy* textbook, the arteries were red, the veins blue, the nerves yellow. But here everything is tan-grey.

I look at a sliver of a nerve marked T→ nested within the brachial plexus. *How do they expect me to know what that is?* It is all a jumble to me, and I realize that I should have studied more, a lot more.

The next morning, my test grade is posted on the hallway wall with everyone else's, for the whole world to see. I failed. Never in my life have I flunked a test, so this is a low point in my academic career, and I take it as a sobering lesson. Looking at the grade on the wall, I never doubt that I can reach my goals of passing "gross" and finishing medical school, but I will have to work a lot harder.

Tootie teaches me that. "The answers are right here. Do the work. Use me. Learn from me."

Hers was a true gift of self. After her death, she is teaching four aspiring physicians. Thank you, Tootie.

3

SUPERFLUITY

The 1970s bring us lava lamps and beaded curtains, VW Beetles and the heart-throb Beatles, marijuana and sexual liberation. This is also the decade in which the birth control pill becomes widely available, CT scanners enter the scene, and the specialty of family practice comes into its own.

Still a first-year medical student, I drive to a medical-school-sponsored free clinic on the west side of San Antonio. Despite my best efforts, my mind swirls with uncertainty and self-doubt. *I don't know how to do anything. I wonder if they will ask me to take a blood pressure or draw blood. Will the faculty physician ask me a lot of questions?* At this point my total medical experience consists of assisting at one mall health fair, completing a few months of classroom work, and beginning gross anatomy and cadaver dissection. My three tank mates and I fondly named our cadaver Tootie, but tonight my patients will be alive.

As I pull my Pinto into the parking area, I note that the building is less a clinic and more an unassuming wooden frame house. It sits in a row of similar structures that line the street, which is also old and worn. This house has been converted to function as a clinic in the part of town most accessible to the needy. The living room is now the patient waiting area, the kitchen an ersatz lab with urine dip sticks, pregnancy tests, and an old worn microscope. This is also the medication room, with a refrigerator and a few shelves off to the side. Two bedrooms have been converted into patient exam rooms, and a third is the consultation area, where we now gather. Sparse though these surroundings are, as we discuss our patients tonight I feel a real sense of purpose. Now my healing career has begun; I will see actual patients for the first time.

This clinic, I soon learn, deals mostly with treating sexually transmitted infections—STIs or venereal disease, as we called it back then—and providing contraception. Although I feel totally unqualified to be seeing them, tonight the patients call me "Doctor." They seem to think that I know what I am doing as they tell me their symptoms and look to me with expectant eyes for help.

I soon find myself sitting on the floor of the consultation room. We are all atop giant pillows covered in bright tie-dyed patterns. In a circle joining me are another first-year med student, a third-year, and our attending, who is a gynecology faculty doctor. Behind him a poster hangs on the wall, colorfully, nay, psychedelically proclaiming the poem, *Desiderata*. "Go placidly amid the noise and haste, and remember what peace there may be in silence," it starts. The same poster adorned my college dorm room—the poem is a 1970s zeitgeist, and I note this evening that, all in all, it is helpful advice for a medical student.

"Jolina is a twenty-four-year-old young woman," I tell my attending physician with all the confidence I can muster, "who comes to the clinic for the birth control pill. She lives with her mother and her two children, ages two and three, and tells me she does not want to get pregnant again. She is looking for a job."

I look up from my notes to see what the doctor has to say.

"Does she have any medical conditions that would make the pill unsafe for her?" he asks me.

I had not known to ask. He turns to the group.

"What more do we need to know about this patient?"

The evening progresses and Jolina receives her care—her prescription, a reminder to use condoms to prevent VD, and a follow-up appointment to check her blood pressure in a month. The third-year student tells me that the patient will likely not return for this. We discuss several more patients, hand out condoms to all who ask, and administer several penicillin shots. At about 10 PM, we call it a night.

I volunteer to stop by the university hospital lab with the box of specimens we have collected. On my long drive uptown, I reflect upon the evening. My first thought is a selfish one: how magnificent it is that I am finally seeing patients. Me, a lowly first-year med student who has dreamed of being a doctor since childhood. I am delighted to have used my meager knowledge tonight and to have learned from my attending. Then, thinking of Jolina and the others, I realize that this has also been my first personal experience with indigent people. They are all about my age but their lives are so different, so harsh and so complicated. This part is unsettling. The poverty and the lifestyle choices of the young patents I saw tonight need fixing, but I do not know how to accomplish that. I hope that someday I will.

Ever the volunteer, I find myself the following week at a free clinic of a totally different nature—the DePaul Family Clinic on the far south side of town. I drive south through town, first a long distance on the highway, and then on ever-narrower and bumpier streets. On either side are houses that startle me. They are wooden shacks, really, each with a door and one or two windows. They look like one-room houses, dubious shelters from Texas's harsh sun. I have never been to this part of town before.

The DePaul Clinic, a Catholic facility built to serve indigent people, is well-staffed by volunteers and by Daughter of Charity nuns in white habits. Here the patients are young and old, male and female, sometimes entire families. The clinic space is larger than the west side clinic, with more exam rooms, and a dedicated drug room with shelves and shelves of free medication. The laboratory has its own volunteer, a middle-aged retired lab technician who is friendly and loves to teach medical students.

My first patient of the evening is Mr. Garcia, who is sitting on the exam table when I enter. He is moderately overweight, with a tired-looking face, clad in a frayed T-shirt and faded jeans. The smell of a hard day's work permeates the room. Three rambunctious children are with him, and I bend down to greet them all, making sure to touch each one to prevent *mal de ojo*. This Mexican superstition is widely held in South Texas and goes something like this: if a child is admired but not physically touched by the admirer, he is stricken with the "evil eye." Bad luck or sickness will most certainly ensue.

Mr. Garcia and I talk, and I take his history, *his story*. A few minutes later, I am sitting at the table in the consultation room, textbooks and teaching models lining the shelves behind me. My attending tonight is a family physician, and I present my patient to him.

"Mr. Garcia is a forty-seven-year-old man," I begin, "who is here because he has run out of his diabetes medication. He usually gets it at the Barrio clinic with his Medicare, but he does not have gas money to drive up there until payday on Friday."

The attending patiently teaches me how to evaluate this man for dangerous signs and symptoms of high blood sugar. We perform a physical examination together and then take him to the lab room to check a finger-stick blood sugar. 285—high but not dangerously so. We give Mr. Garcia a bottle of medication from the shelf.

"*Adios, señor*," I tell him as he rounds up his children to leave.

Driving home on this night I am struck by the superfluity of my life compared to that of the people I have just seen. While I consider my own life to be meager, there is always enough gas for my car, bread and peanut butter to eat, and an apartment roof over my head. How on earth do the people I saw in the clinic live in those worn-down shacks by the side of the road? Then I recall the patients at the free clinic last week, indigent as well but also struggling with social and sexual problems. How on earth can they pull themselves out of their less-than-meager lifestyles? And should I make the huge assumption that they even want to? At least I can keep giving them what care and dignity I have within myself to give.

It strikes me that such a sentiment seems obvious, even trite. On this late night of self-reflection as I drive north to my apartment, I realize that my freshly-imprinted experiences while working at the free clinics have made my life's calling all the more tangible to me.

4

BIRTHDAYS

Imagine a patient who is partially blind, takes medication for seizures, and has had four colon operations. Now imagine that this patient is just twelve months old.

I have not seen Rafael, the little cutie, since he was discharged from our neonatal intensive care unit five months ago, when I was a third-year medical student. As a lowly doctor-in-training, I did not participate in the NICU decision-making or procedures; these tasks were relegated to the residents and neonatal specialists. On the positive side, I learned a lot through osmosis, just being there, and I definitely grew attached to the babies and their parents.

Today we are celebrating our annual party for NICU "graduates." About twenty children, their parents, and a large group of doctors and nurses gather in the hospital conference room. Balloons and streamers greet the guests with bursts of color, as does a banner: "Happy Birthday, Babies!"

This is a joyful event; most parents here today did not know if their newborn children would survive to leave the hospital. For each mom and dad, the earliest memories of their newborn bundle were not as joyful as it is for most. They saw a tiny pink body connected to tubes and lines, perhaps with eyes patched closed to prevent damage from the phototherapy light. The parents reached through holes in the side of the in-cubator to touch their baby's miniature hands, fingers as slender as toothpicks. I remember showing Rafael's mother how to touch the palm of his hand with her index finger—*firmly, like this*—so that he would grasp her finger.

The usual newborn memories that the family missed out on in those first days and weeks nagged at me. There was no wrapping the baby in the hand-knit-ted baby blanket from Aunt Jane, no cuddling the baby and rocking him to sleep in a wooden rocking chair, as mothers have done for centuries. Would it ever happen?

Yes! Here they all are, babies returning to celebrate with the caregivers who all too often do *not* see their patients go home. As I walk into the party room, I feel an unusual sense of grandeur—a pleasant feeling, to be sure, yet one that is hard to put my finger on. It is as if the extreme myopic focus I had adopted while caring for each delicate newborn baby has today been trans-formed by a cosmic hand to open up to a larger view.

God's larger view, this is, which I and the parents could not see back then. These babies, from among all the incubator babies in the NICU, *did* make it home, and it's an invigorating experience for parents and healers alike.

I spot Rafael in his mother's arms from across the room and make my way through the crowd to greet them.

"Happy birthday, sweetie!" I gush at the squirmy infant, as I gently squeeze his foot. "It is so nice to see you both again."

Today Rafael's mother tells me proudly that he is holding his head up on his own and eating baby food from a spoon.

Birthdays are a big part of why I became a doctor. When I was a child, birthdays were huge events for my family, despite our large family, or maybe because of it. We always celebrated in our home, with just immediate family—definitely a large enough gathering with the eight of us. Our small dining room was always festooned gaily with construction-paper loopy chains, balloons, and handmade signs. A red felt crown with gold trim was reserved for the guest of honor.

The most exciting part, however, was the cake. Mom spent hours baking and decorating it. Picture an elaborate castle cake with spires, gumdrop walls, and rock candy paths. A chocolate guitar with licorice strings and miniature plastic Beatles. A piano cake with nougat keys and a tiny sheet of rice-paper music carefully imprinted with food-color musical notes and the title "Happy Birthday, Pam."

For his part, on each birthday Dad would keep us abreast of the historical details of the event we were celebrating.

"Eight years ago at this very moment, Peggy, I was driving your mother to the hospital to have you!"

"Twelve years ago at 7:30 PM, you were born, Pam."

Then there was the birthday birth-day. During Liz's first birthday party, Mom went into labor and shortly—very shortly—afterward delivered Carl. Two birthdays on the same date. Dad loved to tell that story. I don't know how he remembered all the details, except that the entry of each of his children into God's world meant so much to him.

To this day, I keep a scrapbook with fading photos of the parties and cakes and use the decorating ideas with my own children. They are grown now and have caught the birthday party-festooning and cake-decorating bug. There is a real life-affirming family heritage here, passing from generation to generation before my eyes.

As the years passed, my parents did not miss the birth of their grandchildren, even if it meant driving completely across the country. Grandma and

Grandpa were always at the hospital, waiting with joy in the nursery, to see the precious baby they already loved so much. New York, South Carolina, Texas— they were there.

Such love of life was not displayed by my parents on birthdays only; it was their way of life. Dad and Mom taught us by their words and their deeds the importance of treating everyone with respect. Although they would be the first to admit that they were not perfect parents, I consider my upbringing to have been special in that they never uttered derogatory comments or racial epithets and never allowed us to speak disrespectfully of our own brothers or sisters or our teachers and friends. I honestly do not remember them arguing with each other. If it happened, they followed the old adage never to argue in front of the children. Here was another family heritage—a genuine and deeply-held respect for all human life—a heritage that nudged me down the path to becoming a doctor.

Best birthday gift ever!

5

TIRE TREADS

Every parent's worst nightmare came to pass on this day. How many times has a mother or father grabbed their child's hand to stop him from running into a store parking lot or yelled at her not to run into the street to chase a ball?

"Watch out or you'll be hit by a car!"

One Saturday afternoon in the pediatric intensive care unit, I, as the senior medical student, am writing up a patient progress note when we get word that we will soon be receiving an eighteen-month-old from the emergency room. She has just been run over by a car. Her family's car. In the driveway of her home. By her grandmother.

One of the residents heads down to the ER to scope things out and soon returns with the story. A car hit a toddler, Tina, as her grandmother was backing out of the driveway. After being knocked over, she was run over by the rear tire. The car's tire had completely and squarely traversed her thorax, but x-rays taken in the ER showed no broken bones. She appears to be doing well. Tina is being admitted to our service for observation.

The PICU nurses prepare a patient bay for our newest admission, giving me a moment to reflect on the agony that this family must be suffering. Indeed, when the child arrives on the gurney, she is surrounded by crying adults—her parents and her *abuela*, her grandmother. The unit clerk ushers the adults to the family waiting room, so that the pediatric senior resident can examine Tina.

The toddler is disheveled and crying, which is a favorable sign, and looking around at us with alert wide eyes, also a positive finding. We note abrasions and swelling to her cheek, along with fresh bruises on the front of her pelvis. At the foot of the gurney lie her shirt and shorts, cut off her body in the ER. The nurse reports the vital signs, which are all reassuring. The senior resident listens to Tina's chest for heart and lung sounds and palpates her abdomen. Aside from the abrasions and bruises, the child appears in remarkably healthy condition.

"Do you think she was really run over?" the resident asks.

Our attending physician has just arrived, and she reaches to the folded bundle of clothes near Tina's feet. She picks up a faded yellow T-shirt. Across the front are marks that are unmistakable and cause my eyes to widen: an eight-inch black line of zigzag tire treads. Tire treads? How is this girl still alive?

The attending explains that the walls of an eighteen-month-old child's thorax—indeed all the bony structures—are still mostly cartilage, not bone at all. So, as the car tire ran over Tina's body, her chest literally compressed downward and then bounced back.

"What we must do now is keep an eye on her heart and lungs and abdomen, to watch for signs of damage."

The resident starts an IV to have a line open in case of occult bleeding from her liver or spleen. We run blood tests, echocardiogram, abdominal ultrasound, and repeat x-rays. The attending gives the family an update every few hours, and each time I remain behind afterward. Her family is there continuously, and I get to know them, especially the grandmother. I am just the medical student, the lowest member of the unit hierarchy, but at least I can talk to the family. It really is true, the aphorism that medical students have the least knowledge and experience of any member on the healthcare team, but they often spend the most time talking with the patient and family.

So I sit with Tina's grandmother in the family waiting room and at her *niña's* bedside. Abuela is a petite and gentle Hispanic woman, her faced lined with years of care and worry. A pearl rosary is constantly intertwined in her arthritic fingers.

That evening Tina's blood pressure begins to drop. Knowing that this may be a sign of internal bleeding, the resident orders her IV fluid rate to be increased and obtains another ultrasound of her liver and spleen. The operating room staff is notified of a possible case. The only way to know if she has more subtle bleeding is for the surgeon to open her abdomen for exploration. Before this becomes necessary, however, her blood pressure returns to the normal range, as do our own adrenaline levels.

I reassure Abuela, in her grief and unimaginable guilt, that Tina is now doing well. She tells me that they were celebrating Tina's older sister's *quinceañera*, her fifteenth birthday party and a coming-out ritual in the Hispanic culture. The grandmother proudly tells me that all her grandchildren have turned out very well and she will be a great-grandmother very soon. Midafternoon on the day of the party, she got into her car to return to her own home.

Over and over Abuela tells me plaintively, "I did not know she was back there. How could I know she was back there? *Dios mio*, is she going to die?"

As the next few days progress, Tina continues to do well. She sits up in bed and on the third day is eating normal infant foods with gusto. This, of course, pleases Abuela, and I am reminded how food and love and health are all intertwined for grandmothers worldwide. The PICU attending continues to give encouraging news to Tina's family, and soon our resilient patient is ready for discharge to home.

We are all elated to be sending Tina home, especially after remembering the horror of that first day, when a family celebration turned into a life-threatening emergency in a mere few seconds. Was Tina's survival a miracle or simply flexible infant anatomy? Opinions may vary, but to me they are one and the same. Tina survived being run over by a car, and Abuela tells me that she knows God answered their prayers.

6

THE TRUTH ABOUT CLOUDS

The clouds fluff up in the blue Texas sky, rising from the flat dusty horizon. Their glittery billows catch the morning sun as I walk toward the airport terminal building, my white lab coat slung across my arm and black medical bag in hand. An open hangar stands to my right, stark and isolated, and the airstrip is just beyond. A momentary thrill rises in my chest as a red and white prop-job rushes down the runway and takes off. Shielding my eyes from the sun, I stop to watch the plane rise until it disappears into the clouds.

For a moment, I am a seven-year-old girl again, sitting behind my father in the back seat of our wood-paneled station wagon. A career Air Force pilot, Dad's idea of a fun Sunday afternoon for his family was to pile the eight of us into the car, park near the edge of the base runway, and together watch the "birds" come and go. Each airplane sparked an artful tale, just for us children, about where in the world it had flown and what its job was in keeping America safe. My father was my hero, and the planes were magical.

Born just outside a Strategic Air Command center, I grew up on Air Force bases during the height of the Cold War. We military brats were accustomed to the sound of sonic booms and jets zooming overhead as we played jump rope in the back yard. Huge lumbering cargo planes lifted off above us. Perched on one foot in a hopscotch square, looking skyward, I wondered how on earth something that huge could fly.

So, I can't help the sense of excitement today as the plane takes off and soars above my head. I am beginning my ophthalmology elective as a fourth-year medical student, and my attending physician, a pediatric ophthalmologist, is a pilot. He is not just a pilot, but a philanthropic pilot. Dozens of counties in Texas do not have a physician, he told me when I started the rotation. He does his part by flying to the southern part of Texas on Saturdays to care for children with eye problems.

Today the three of us—the doc-cum-pilot, another medical student, and I—meet in the terminal building and then stand at the desk for a moment while he files his flight plan. Carrying cardboard boxes full of medical supplies, we walk out to the plane. As I climb into the right front seat, the physician, clad in a green flight jacket, walks around the plane performing his pre-flight safety routine. He goes down the written list on his clipboard, pencils in check marks, and then gives a thumbs-up to the attendant who is fueling the plane.

The Cessna is a four-seater and not air-conditioned. While we await the okay from the tower to take off, heat rises up from the asphalt and beads of sweat break out on my forehead. I know that we will cool off when we reach altitude, and the excitement of flying today is well worth the perspiration. We taxi over the bumpy baked surface to the runway, where the pilot opens the throttle, and we gain speed. Scrub trees out my side window go by in a blur, faster, and faster still. The ride suddenly becomes smooth as we lift off into the heavens.

As we pass through a layer of fluffy clouds, I think again of my father and the day in the station wagon when he told me, "No, honey, if you were up there in the sky, you could *not* bounce on the clouds like you jump on your bed."

He spoke in his matter-of-fact voice, his teaching voice, not realizing what his words meant to me. My childhood disappointment at that moment had been immeasurable as I learned the awful truth. Clouds are just water vapor, like the heavy fog we sometimes see on the ground, he explained further. But my young imagination had always thought that they were giant, shimmering, plush balls of cotton. I remember feeling sad for the baby angels in heaven: no billowy bounces, no puffy pillow fights.

The cherubs that I should be thinking about today, however, are the earth-bound ones. The pilot follows IH 35 south for an hour or so and then veers west toward our destination, a tiny airstrip atop a desolate mesquite-covered plain. When we land, the county nurse, a middle-aged woman in a denim jumper, walks out to the plane to greet us. She sports a friendly smile as she ushers us to a government van. After a brief, but again bumpy, ride to the county health office, which is actually a trailer next to the sheriff's office, I wonder what lies ahead for us that day.

The nurse explains that the health office staff members provide immunizations to the local children and adults and telephone advice for the sick and injured, but there is no doctor. The rural residents look forward to the Saturday visits from the eye doctor, and our schedule today is filled.

As we talk, the trailer door creaks open to reveal Jesus, a thin seven-year-old wearing a Houston Oilers T-shirt and a dark blue patch over his left eye. He grins shyly at us as he holds the door open so that his mother can push inside a baby stroller carrying his sister.

As we bring him into the tiny exam room, the ophthalmologist asks, "So, how is our brave pirate today, arrrgh?"

The doctor removes the eye patch, and I see Jesus's other eye move outward, revealing his strabismus. The ophthalmologist then performs a visual acuity test and demonstrates, for my benefit, how to do a cover/uncover test of the eye musculature. He tells me that he had hoped that Jesus's weaker eye would strengthen if the stronger one was patched for a few months, but today we see that has not happened. Speaking to the mother in Spanish, he explains that her son needs eye muscle surgery, and he describes the procedure to her in simple terms. Together they make plans to do the surgery in San Antonio in a few weeks.

We see several more children with strabismus this morning, and I improve my examination skills and knowledge of eye muscle innervations. Next come two children with conjunctivitis, another with a sty, and our morning session is done.

During our lunch break, I ask the nurse more questions about the patients who are served by this clinic. The families who live in this area, she tells me, are mostly farmers and ranchers and the people they employ. Many are indigent, and for them medical care is a luxury. There is no local physician, so the people here are used to phone-based care or self-treatment or no treatment. Because of the huge void in medical care for both chronic and acute conditions, many patients must drive one or two counties from their homes to see a doctor. That is, the nurse tells me, if they have enough money to buy gas for their car. Or if they even have a car.

Another childhood memory pushes its way to my mind's eye as she and I sit at the wooden table, shading ourselves from the harsh Texas sun under a cluster of pecan trees. A black-and-white TV screen flickers the image of a serious-looking man's face. The evening news was a ritual in our home, and ten-year-old me generally ignored it. But that night the newsman reported an event that seemed worthy of my attention: there was a new war, a "war on poverty." I looked up from my homework to see President Johnson speaking to the entire country from the White House in Washington, DC, and then stark images of dilapidated buildings and children in tattered clothes. At that very moment, I now recall, my one thought was crystal clear: in a few years, at least by the time I grow up, there will be no more poor people. The President said so.

"Mom, did you hear that? The President is going to end poverty—no more poor people!" She smiled and kept frying the pork chops.

My plane trips to the poorest parts of Texas give me my first close-up look at rural medicine and open my heart to the massive amount of work that is still needed to help the children that live there. It is a life-changing experience for a young medical student—traveling upward through the clouds, rising closer to the heavens, and then landing on a dry, desolate piece of earth to care for the local children. They are like baby angels growing up in a harsh world, a world in which, at least during my lifetime, poverty will exist. Perhaps our presence today cushions their lives just a bit. As my mother knew so long ago, the war on poverty belongs not to the President, but to us all.

7

GOOD SAMARITAN

The man from Samaria in the Bible parable, walking alone on a road, came upon an injured man lying crumpled on the ground. He had been robbed and beaten. While others had passed by the victim without concern, this man stopped to help and saved the life of a person he did not know. Flash forward two thousand years, and we see that kindness to strangers is still a valued ideal in our culture today.

A physician is always a physician, no matter the place, the time, or the circumstance. For all doctors, there are situations outside of the hospital or clinic that call into use the MD after our names. Even without my black bag of medical supplies, in most cases all that is needed is a cool head, common sense, and basic first aid.

Quality time with my new husband is all that is on my mind as we meander, hand-in-hand, through the colorful pathways of Disneyland. It is our honeymoon, a cool March morning in the early 1980s, and we have just enjoyed a few of the attractions. Walking toward a snack area, we notice a commotion and a young lady sitting on the ground. I ask a security guard if she needs a doctor.

He responds by declaring loudly to all around us, "Clear the way. This man is a doctor."

He takes my husband's arm to escort him to the lady on the ground. Hmmmmm.

After my husband tells the guard that his wife is the doctor, I kneel down to assess the lady. I talk to her a bit, take her pulse, and help her to a shaded area to lie down. A cool drink and relief from the sun is all that she needs, and she thanks me sweetly for my assistance.

Of all the strange coincidences, I think as I sit in the bleachers at a high-school football game. It is my alma mater, and I am playing the glockenspiel with our alumni band. Just before halftime, a cheerleader comes up the steps to tell me that another cheerleader is having an asthma attack—would I please come to the field house to help? As it turns out, the ill girl is a patient of mine. A week ago, I saw her in my clinic for her asthma, and we had talked about the upcoming game.

So Callie calls for my help that afternoon, and as I enter field house she is sitting upright on a cot, hot and sweaty and struggling to breathe. Her skin is still pink, but her pulse and respiration rates are elevated. I instruct one of the girls to call 9-1-1 and another to get Callie a glass of water. Callie tells me that she had last used her inhaler about two hours ago, and we find the unit in her purse to give her another dose. Still, she remains short of breath, and thankfully the EMTs arrive within a few minutes. In short order, they set her up with oxygen and a nebulizer treatment, as they transfer her to a gurney for a trip to the hospital.

When I call her home the next morning, her mother thanks me for my help and tells me that Callie is doing much better after some medication adjustment. Go, team, go!

As I drive home from Sunday Mass with my elderly mother next to me, the early afternoon is just starting to heat up. Dad died a few years ago, so my sisters and I take turns picking Mom up at our childhood home and going to church with her.

As we exit the highway near her neighborhood, I notice up ahead on the side of the road the thin shape of a man. He is stooped over, stumbling, looking as if he is about to fall to the ground. Other cars are passing him by, so I carefully maneuver my car across three lanes to get to him. I hand Mom my cell phone to call 9-1-1 and go over to the man, reaching him just as he slumps to the hard gravel. He is still conscious and still breathing, but pale. His skin and tongue are dry, and his ribs are visible each time he takes a breath—a sign of respiratory distress. On his arm is a plastic hospital ID bracelet with yesterday's date on it.

The only aid I can provide him as we await the ambulance is shade from the hot sun using my body, words of comfort, and my medical expertise. I watch him closely for signs of heart or lung failure, and he remains stable. The EMTs tell me that he is a local homeless man who is in and out of the hospital for reasons unknown to us all. Back to the hospital they take him.

I doubt there is any physician who has not stopped at the scene of a motor vehicle accident. I have had my share. The level of injury can vary from just shaken up to severely injured, but I always lend my expertise until the EMTs arrive to take over. Perhaps the best lesson I have learned from happening upon many an accident is this: I always ask myself *Is there already an ambulance on the scene?* Here is the point, which may save a few bruised physician egos: if the EMTs are already there and caring for the victim, they do not need the help of a passing physician, even one trained in cardiopulmonary resuscitation and military trauma casualty management. This was a hard-learned lesson for me as a newly minted physician, and I made the mistake only twice before I realized that my presence was superfluous. More than one EMT rudely treated me as such, to the point of ignoring me. So, I always stop at an accident when there is an apparently injured person and no rescuers on the scene. Conversely, I never stop if the ambulance has arrived.

Not paying much attention to the people around me one Sunday morning in church, I am singing a hymn, lost in other-worldly thoughts.

A loud voice rises from behind me, "Is there a doctor in the church?"

The priest stops speaking.

I turn around and then rapidly make my way to a cluster of people who are surrounding an old-looking man. He is in a sitting position, but slumped forward. The people around him tell me that he passed out but regained consciousness in the few seconds it took me to reach him. I tell him that I am a doctor and ask the crowd to please move back to "give him some air."

The pulse in his wrist is reassuringly strong and regular. I ask him to lie down in the pew, but he refuses, proclaiming that he does not need any help. He insists that he was just dizzy because he skipped breakfast for Communion. I continue my evaluation: ABCs—check; no chest pain, no breathing difficulty—check; no fruity breath—check. He continues to perk up, and declines to have us call 9-1-1 for a more in-depth check, opting instead to have his son take him home to eat breakfast. Mass resumes after the brief pause.

Later in the day, I call him at his home, and he tells me he is feeling better. He continues to seem irritated at my "making such a fuss" and expresses no appreciation to me or the others who had helped him. But that is no problem. My care to him that Sunday morning was from my heart; it was not a deed requiring reward.

Strained and bruised extremities are common occurrences for doctors who are also parents involved in their child's activities. When a runner falls during a middle-school track meet and twists his ankle, the coach looks to me in the bleachers for care and advice. When a child scrapes her wrist on the school playground, the office secretary, remembering that I am volunteering in the library that afternoon, calls for my help.

She knows, as I do, that a doctor is always a doctor. I view my medical education as a privilege and a badge to wear at all times. Kindness to people we know and those we do not know becomes a gift to both the giver and the recipient.

8

NEWBORN

One April afternoon, I sat with my sisters on the davenport of our living room. Our sneakers and play dresses formed a colorful squirmy montage, and as the oldest at age nine, I had positioned myself smack in the middle.

"Mom's coming home with the new baby!" someone whispered.

A hushed response floated back as we practiced our new-baby-in-the-house voices. "I wonder if he will be crying!"

Growing up in a large family, we knew we would each get our turn to hold the baby gently with pillows under our arms *(don't touch her soft spot!)*. We would help with the diaper changes and powdering and even dab an alcohol-soaked cotton ball to the umbilical cord to help it dry out *(no, it does not hurt the baby)*. When the cord and clamp fell off after a week, we children found it a cause for cheers.

"A house with a baby is a happy house," my mother often said.

She said the same about music, and I know now that all things sweet and gentle were intertwined in her heart to make us a close-knit family. The smell of baby powder, the sound of cooing, even the sight of the bassinette heaped with pastel blankets, all mingled in my young mind as a celebration of new life.

Many years later during my obstetrics rotation as a third-year family practice resident, I am on night call in the hospital when Mrs. Norman, a twenty-four-year-old pregnant woman, presents to the labor deck in active labor. As it happens, I have been following her through this, her first pregnancy, which has gone smoothly. Earlier today in my clinic, she was having irregular contractions and told me that she had dispelled her mucous plug that morning.

"It won't be long now," I recall telling her and her husband.

Tonight, I examine her and note that her is cervix four centimeters dilated, which is normal for early labor. A nurse applies the external uterine and fetal monitor belts to her abdomen, and another starts an IV. I see that the fetal heart tracing is reassuring, with a baseline of 150-160 beats per minute and healthy variability. Mom's spontaneous contractions are strong, about every minute, and during each contraction the baby's heart rate slows temporarily to 60 bpm.

Because of the decelerations, I need to better monitor the baby, so I rupture the amniotic membranes and place a fetal scalp electrode. The return of clear amniotic fluid indicates that the baby has not been in distress and has not released stool. IV fluids and an oxygen mask for the mother decreases the contractions to every two minutes or so, and the decels become less frequent as well, dipping only to 90 bpm.

Mom is more comfortable. She, her husband, and I discuss what is happening to her baby as the next few hours progress. They tell me about the baby room they have decorated in yellow and green and about her mother's plan to arrive in town soon to help for a few weeks. I call the obstetrics staff doctor at home, and he agrees with the plan to continue to observe and support our two patients.

Her cervix is opening rapidly, and the fetal heart rate tracing begins to show more persistent slowing. I position the mother on her left side, and the baby's heart rate improves for a time. When it worsens again, I call the obstetrician and ask him to come in to the hospital to examine the tracing. By the time he arrives, the tracing has again become favorable, and we stand at her bedside together, watching the tracing carefully, second by second. When the decels return, our impression is that there is probably significant umbilical cord compression by the descending baby and that an immediate C-section is the best course of action. As the obstetrician prepares the mother, I speak with Mr. Norman, telling him of our concerns and our plan. He nods at me in assent.

Within ten minutes of our arrival in the operating room, the baby is delivered, with the obstetrician as primary surgeon and me as his first assistant. The newborn is pale and a bit floppy but moving, with a whimper for a cry, as I hand him off to the pediatrician. The nurse rubs the baby vigorously with a scrub towel to stimulate him to cry and breathe, and I listen as they assess the baby. We all breathe a sigh of relief as the baby screams; he is a little fighter!

When I join Mrs. Norman in her hospital room a few hours later, she is physically and emotionally exhausted, and I have to admit that I am as well. We speak quietly, chatting with her husband and her mother, who has just arrived. I pass along my congratulations and then step back as the nurse brings in the baby, wrapped in a blue blanket.

"Hello, sweet Evan," the new mother coos lovingly to the baby at her breast.

"Evan from heaven!" adds Mr. Norman. "That's what you are. You sure gave us a scare, but here you are."

He kisses his son's rosy cheeks.

Long ago, we sisters, five in all, sat together, waiting for our new baby brother to arrive home in our father's arms. From this experience, I learned firsthand that each precious newborn is to be cherished and pampered and fussed over. I was too young then to know that not all babies receive such love, too young to realize the awful truth about broken families, child abuse, even abortion. When the time came for me to face these realities, the values I had learned as a young girl became strong convictions to guide me to act compassionately.

9

MESSES

Acts of love can be philanthropic feats that make the headlines of the newspaper, or they can be so trivial that we do not even recognize them.

Mother Teresa reminded us that, "Not all of us can do great things. But we can do small things with great love."

When I was very young, before I was old enough to change my baby sisters' and brothers' diapers, my mother cleaned dirty cloth diapers in the toilet. Picture it: my mother in a skirt and low-heel pumps, kneeling beside the toilet, the corner of the white cloth in her hand, swishing and swirling it up and down in the toilet water. The brown gooey glob made its way inch by inch into the water. Then she used both hands to wring out the diaper and place it in the pail, at the same time giving the knob a flush with her elbow. Her hands, so sweet and motherly, did this smelly, drippy chore countless times for her six children, while at the same time there was a gentle smile on her face. Every time.

What I remember today about her smile was my thinking, *She looks like she is having fun. I want to do that!* But when I asked, she told me that I was not old enough yet to clean messy diapers. That was what she called them: messes. But what I could do was check the kids' diapers for her.

"Pam, would you please see if your sister has a mess in her diaper?"

Later, when I was grown, I shared that memory with my mother. She told me that she always prayed when she did unpleasant chores, to transform them into an act of love and thanksgiving.

"Thank you, God, for this healthy child."

"Thank you for our beautiful family that I love so much."

"I am so grateful for this home and for plumbing that works."

Many has been the time, and any medical student or intern can relate to this, that I receive the dreaded call to report to the emergency room to do a disimpaction. A chronically constipated patient, usually elderly, is in severe pain due to not having had a bowel movement for a prolonged time. This is a perfect job for the intern—the hard balls of stool must be scooped out with gloved fingers to relieve the patient's pain. There is virtually no chance of harming the patient in the process. In fact, the patient will feel a lot better than the intern when it is all over. The job is smelly and unpleasant and, yes, *messy.*

One morning I admit a patient to the hospital, a man with alcoholic liver cirrhosis and a six-inch abscess on his left thigh. This infection must be drained and packed with strips of medicated cloth to allow it to heal properly. After the patient is prepped and I don the disposable gown, gloves, and goggles, I incise the tense red-purple mass with an 11-blade. Instantaneously a stench is released into the room, an odor so overpowering that I must stop what I am doing. I freeze. At the same moment, a large drop of the pus flies up to meet my goggles squarely in my line of vision. It takes an incredible amount of fortitude and a bit of prayer for me to finish, but finish I do, draining and packing that miasmic mess.

A few years later, I am doing a routine pelvic exam on a young woman while I myself am three months pregnant. The patient tells me that she has been having a foul-smelling vaginal discharge, and I silently agree as I begin the pelvic exam. After inserting the speculum, I notice an old tampon lodged deep inside, and the foul smell turns my stomach. As I ask my nurse to hand me a long-handled clamp so I can extract it, I stifle a pregnancy-induced urge to vomit. The very next moment, I *do* vomit, but swallow it discreetly and continue removing the old tampon. Messy.

Physicians do such tasks: we clean up messes as part of our calling to help our patients. These acts that assault our senses are as much a part of healing as are the more glamorous ones. We do the unpleasant tasks because we care about every one of our patients. Every time.

10

RAGDOLL

Adriana started making the Raggedy Ann doll on the day that I told her she was pregnant. In her early twenties and from a broken home, she values her new growing family above all else. Her husband, a Navy sailor, is serving overseas on an unaccompanied tour, and she misses Robert enormously. Adriana has time on her hands and a creative spirit, so she cuts each piece of muslin with happiness, and then stitches it into place with joy.

At every visit to my clinic she pleads with me, "Please, Dr. Camosy, can't you get my husband home?"

Unfortunately for her and for multitudes of military wives, a pregnancy is not a reason to end an overseas tour and bring the father-to-be home. My heart saddens every time I must tell a patient this.

Early in her pregnancy, when she learns that I, too, am a crafter, she brings the cloth pieces of the ragdoll to her prenatal appointments to show me as the project develops—a white cloth arm and hand here, now the flowery pinafore dress, then the pretty red yarn hair braided just right. She has thrown herself into making the ragdoll, and it seems to help her deal with her pregnancy alone, without the man she loves by her side to share the excitement.

At each prenatal visit, I measure her abdomen and tell her that the number of centimeters is just right for the weeks of her pregnancy. We hug each other when I first hear the baby's heartbeat with my fetoscope. Her abdomen grows nicely, the fetal movement is reassuring, and at her appointments I let her listen to the heartbeat. With my hands, I can show her just where I feel her baby's head, bottom, feet.

Adriana completes the Raggedy Ann doll when she is seven months pregnant. She brings it to her next appointment, and my clinic staff and I are all smiles. The doll is crisp and smiling and lovely, about the size of a real baby. With the help of a few other wives from her husband's squadron, she tells us, she set up the baby's crib in a corner of their apartment bedroom.

She asks me again, this time with tears in her eyes, "Can't you get my husband home? I really need him here when I go into labor."

One day, she calls the clinic to report that she has not felt her baby move all morning, and I agree to meet her on the obstetrics ward. When I cannot find the baby's heartbeat with the Doppler scope, we go down to Radiology for a formal ultrasound, both of us on the verge of panic. There is no cardiac activity, the radiologist tells us, and it appears that the cord is wrapped around the baby's neck.

"The baby has died," I tell Adriana gently. "I am so sorry."

In medical terms, it is an intra-uterine fetal demise, in lay terms, a stillbirth, and in human terms, a tragedy. Ironically, now I can bring her husband home. Through the American Red Cross office at the hospital, I speak with her husband via telephone on my end and radio on his. The connection is garbled and full of static because he is in the field, but I am able to tell Robert the sad news. I assure him that I will take care of his wife until he can return stateside. His commanding officer and the Red Cross will arrange his immediate flight home. My healer's heart is breaking.

Before he returns home from overseas, though, their baby—their dead baby—must be delivered. With the guidance of the obstetrician on duty and with heaviness in all our hearts, we administer pitocin into Adriana's veins to stimulate her uterus to contract. Adriana's mother and one of the labor nurses stay with her continuously, each holding one of her hands. She is scared, and I must say that I am as well. This is a first for me, after having delivering dozens of babies who were more or less healthy but all alive.

I ask Adriana if she wants to see the baby (yes, she does) and if she wants the baby baptized (also, yes). Less than an hour later, I deliver the pale limp baby, a boy, with the umbilical cord tight around his neck. The nurse wraps him in a blanket and places an ivory-colored stockinette cap on his head. She gives the little angel to his mother to hold, to make a memory, to say goodbye.

"Hello, my Jason," Adriana murmurs.

Every one of us had tears in our eyes as we witness this precious life taken far too soon.

A blue plastic basin of water is set next to Adriana, and the nurse pours water over the pale forehead, reciting "I baptize you in the name of the Father and the Son and the Holy Spirit. Amen."

"Amen," I say to myself. "God, he's yours now."

Adriana and Robert are finally reunited a few days later. Her handmade Raggedy Ann doll is now a symbol of their broken hearts, so they give it to me. They want to remove the sad reminder and to thank me for my care. It is the most special gift a patient has ever given me. The doll and Adriana's story are still with me thirty years later.

11

BRASS KNUCKLES

A teenager dressed in a black T-shirt and black leather pants and sporting brass knuckles on his right hand catches the eye of everyone in my clinic. I notice him out of the corner of my eye as my nurse escorts him down the hall to the exam room. My alarm sensors heightened, I go with her into the exam room and leave the door open. He plops down into the chair, and now I see his sullen facial expression, mostly covered with dark-dyed hair. His is not a particularly threatening demeanor, except for the hardware on his hand.

"Good morning," I say to the teen. "I'm Dr. Camosy."

No answer, except that lack of response is in itself a response. He looks at me with dark eyes lined in black.

I glance at his chart and then tell him, "Brian, we are happy to have you in our clinic today, and I will take care of you soon. But we cannot have brass knuckles in our clinic. Is your car outside? Can you put them back there?"

He nods, mumbles, "Sure," and then walks out to his car.

When I enter the exam room a few minutes later, he is slouched in the chair, weapon-free.

"Hi, Brian, it's nice to meet you. Welcome to our clinic."

I extend my hand, which he shakes tentatively. As I sit down and adjust his chart on the desk, I take another moment to assess my young patient. There is a real person beneath the tough-guy façade that he is presenting to me and to the world.

Pushing the chart and my pen to the side, I look at him and ask, "What can I do for you today?"

"Um, my throat hurts."

After a series of questions and curt answers, I determine that he has been sick for three or four days with a sore throat and stuffy nose. Most bothersome to him is a cough, which is disruptive to the point that he has had to leave the classroom. Yes, he has tried Tylenol and cough drops. No, he does not have a fever, and no one else in his family is sick. It is a history that I really have to work for.

"May I check you over?" I ask. "Let's see what is causing you to feel so crummy."

He nods. I approach him slowly, otoscope in hand. Pulling back his ear to enable me to focus the light through his ear canal, I venture a bit of social history.

"So, where do you go to school?"

Like many teenagers, he responds a bit more energetically when my questions are not face-to-face, but off-handed and casual.

After I listen to his heart and lungs, I ask, "Do you smoke, Brian?" Now I have said his name three times, a self-imposed minimum for every one of my patient encounters.

As the visit unfolds, he appears to relax a bit, to shed a small measure of his reluctance to talk with me. It feels as if I have passed some sort of test. He is daring me to care for him, to really *care* and not just go through the motions.

"It looks as if you have picked up the virus that is going around," I tell him as we sit down in the chairs.

We discuss my plan: rest, plenty of fluids, and cough drops for class time. His assent comes in the form of nods, and he has no questions for me when I ask.

Our time together nearing a close, I realize that I have just scratched the surface of getting to know him, and him, me. But that is my plan for the first visit with my adolescent and teen patients—initiate the relationship, establish trust, and go slowly.

I let them know I care about them and that I am here if they need me. Teenagers do not usually come to my clinic with weapons, as Brian did, but they often have invisible shields that I must deal with before a healing relationship can begin. That will require a few clinic visits.

As Brian and I walk to the front desk, I hand him my business card and invite him to call me if he needs anything. It is a rather adult gesture, and this is not lost on Brian. He smiles slightly and tucks the card into his wallet. A smile—touchdown.

12

SUDDENLY

Just before 7 AM, my overnight emergency room shift is winding down. As I bend over the grey steel desk, putting the finishing touches on my paperwork, a dark blur of motion causes me to look up. A man, sweaty and trembling, is running toward me.

He is carrying a limp, pale, blue-lipped baby, and with a panicked voice he chokes out, "I found her like this in her crib."

I look at the baby's face, her delicate sweet features, and feel a profound pang deep in my chest. I immediately turn off this emotion, take the baby from her father, and rush toward the closest ER bed.

One of the most difficult mental skills I learned as a young physician was to turn off my emotions in an emergency and turn on the intellectual part of my brain. It is most definitely not as easy as using the on-off light switch on the kitchen wall, but the ability comes with experience. So, as I carry the baby, I begin giving orders to my ER team, clearly and emphatically. I use each person's name to avoid confusion: Susy-get-the-crash-cart; Barbara-get-a-pedi-AMBU-bag; John-and-Eloise-start-an-IV-in-each-arm; Charles-call-anesthesia.

I give the baby respirations through a soft plastic mask as the nurse compresses the small chest. Our patient's color never improves despite arm pulses that the corpsman feels with each chest compression. The technician places electrocardiogram leads, and at the same time the nurse achieves intravenous access for medication. Within a few minutes of the child's arrival, the anesthesiologist arrives to take my place at the head of the gurney. He intubates her—places a tube through her mouth and down into her main bronchus. This allows him to breathe for her more effectively with a bag-mask-tube apparatus.

As we suspect, the EKG reveals that there is no cardiac activity of any kind. The nurse continues chest compressions, as the anesthesiologist bags the baby. With each dose of epinephrine into her veins, we hope against hope for a response from the heart tissue, but none comes. Together we attempt to resuscitate the baby for over forty-five minutes. Despite the effort by team members with collective decades of experience, we never get even a hint of a rhythm on the heart monitor.

When I finally call the code and pronounce the time of death, each of us is still full of adrenaline, our brains still in intellectual hyperdrive. We stand in silence for a few moments, looking at the tiny lifeless form on the huge white bed. I find myself sighing deeply, involuntarily, releasing a wave of tension. The nurses and medics join me, I imagine, in switching off the intellectual fight-or-flight instinct, each in their own way. This fight is over.

We now turn to the emotional impact of the situation.

"What was her name?" I ask the charge nurse.

She consults the clipboard, then her eyes meet mine. "Lilly."

I walk through the ER toward the waiting room, feeling physically laden with the failure of the resuscitation and collecting my thoughts for what lies just ahead. As I sit down next to the baby's father and mother, I turn my compassionate side back on.

"My team and I tried our best," I tell them gently, "but we were not able to save Lilly. I am so sorry."

I put one hand briefly on each of their hands in their laps, and we sit quietly. The mother begins to cry, and tears well up in my eyes. I do not try to hide my own sadness from them, as I explain that their baby girl died of crib death, also called sudden infant death syndrome. We do not know why it happens to some babies, but we do know that it is no one's fault. I ask them if they have any questions and if they want to see their daughter.

The three of us walk in silence back into the ER, my heart heavier still. The staff clears the way for us with tender looks on their faces, and we approach the child. The nurses have straightened up to make for a less-distressing viewing by the parents. Used IV and med packages are gone from the gurney and the floor, and EKG wires from her tiny chest. One nurse has tidied the baby's hair and clothes. Lilly's parents are still crying as they touch her tiny hands and bend down to kiss her cheek for their last goodbye.

I think of Lilly and her family frequently, ruefully, over the next few days. This was not my first SIDS baby, nor would it be my last, but each baby's death "diminishes me." My own heart is compressed by a most unsettling set of emotions: not quite guilt, but a definite measure of regret and disappointment. I wish for a momentary alternate universe in which the outcome of our resuscitation would be different. I add a new question to my list to ask God when I get to heaven. Why does he allow babies to die?

Lilly's mother touches me deeply when she calls to invite me to the funeral of their precious daughter. More questions arise in my mind. *How will the family and their friends receive me? Do they blame me in any way?*

The answers are revealed soon after I enter the darkened candlelit sanctuary. To this day I marvel at the graciousness of Lilly's parents. There are hugs all around, and it feels like a silent acknowledgment that we all have been through a tragic experience together. They seem to know that I am grieving, too. How selfless and how gracious they are, at this lowest time of their lives. They continue their kindness to me, introducing me to their family and friends as "Lilly's doctor," rather than—as I was dreading—"the doctor who tried to save Lilly."

Clearly, the healing has already started for Lilly's parents, and they are helping me to heal as well.

13

MYSTERY

Nestled behind the green-plaid living room chair, I felt more content than ever before in all my ten years. Ignoring the hard wall against my back and the scratchy carpet beneath my crisscrossed legs, I stuck the end of a candy cane into my mouth and picked up the rectangular gift in my lap. Here was the best present ever, a new Dana Girl mystery book.

I opened the book and felt its fresh crisp pages. Its title—*The Mystery of the Rusty Key*—coyly enticed me. Here in my very hands was a mystery that must be solved, and I was going to solve it. I looked at the first blank page, which was not really blank at all. My father's neatly penned words sang out to me, adding importance to my experience today behind the chair.

"The Mystery of the Rusty Key," sent with love from Mom and me. Christmas 1965

The first few sentences of the book drew open a stage curtain in my mind. The wood-paneled college dormitory room was familiar to me by now. So were the two sisters who had an uncanny knack for stumbling upon thefts, treachery, even an occasional murder. The pages flew by, and I was transformed into a sophisticated college student in New England. With my keen eye and stealthy footsteps, I explored attics, lecture hall buildings, and wooded clearings, searching for clues. Over the past few years, the sisters and I have solved together *The Secret of the Jade Ring*, *The Clue in the Ivy*, and *The Winking Ruby Mystery*.

The day-to-day work of family medicine reminds me of such mysteries. In fact, I distinctly remember my first day as a practicing physician after my three-year residency ended. Gone was the easy jaunt down the hallway to ask my attending a question. I would have to decide for myself which antibiotic to use for a penicillin-allergic smoker with pneumonia and whether this child's broken arm required an orthopedic consult or simply casting and follow-up in my clinic.

Intellectual and deductive challenges surround even the simplest of patient encounters. Behind the next exam-room door, there is a new puzzle. My choice of family medicine as my life's work ensures that patients come to me with literally any complaint imaginable. Such variation, the mystery of it all, is a huge part of why I find my specialty so *special*.

Why is seven-year-old Jason coughing? He and his mother (the victim and the witness in the world of the Dana Girls) respond to my questions with their answers (my clues). No, he does not cough at night or have a stuffy nose, fever, or a history of allergies. Yes, he coughs when he runs and feels tightness in his chest (my first solid lead). His physical examination is normal today (a dead end that must be explored). His chest x-ray and pulmonary function testing (the forensic evidence) allow me to solve the mystery, and I diagnose exercised-induced cough-variant asthma. We have our culprit.

Why is Mr. Acosta, a diabetic, suddenly having low blood sugar attacks every? He is taking his medication as directed, and his activity level and meals have not changed. After a few minutes of mental head-scratching, I ask him, "Do you eat grapefruit, by any chance?" He tells me that his aunt brought back a case from her trip to Florida, and he has been eating grapefruit every morning for the past week. *The Mystery of the Low Blood Sugar* is solved. I explain to him that the grapefruit is causing his blood levels of the diabetes pill to rise, and his blood sugar to drop. We have caught our perpetrator.

Why is Mrs. Jenson having chest pain? What is this swelling and pain just below Michael's knee cap? Why does Mr. Ramirez urinate over ten times every day?

My clinic sessions, ER shifts, and morning ward rounds provide continual opportunities to use the detective skills that I discovered as a young girl and honed in medical school. *The Clue in the Lung Exam. The Secret of the Patellar Tendon. The Polyuria Mystery.*

Long ago, nestled in my childhood reading nook, I was oblivious to the room around me and even to the sweet peppermint candy in my mouth. The words, paragraphs, and pages of *The Mystery of the Rusty Key* whirred by. Chapter led to chapter, and the candy cane became shorter. The college sisters questioned their witnesses and collected clues. Only after my mother called out to remind me that it was time for dinner did I realize that several hours had passed. Peeking out from behind the chair at the twinkling Christmas tree, I recognized the familiar aroma of bratwurst and potato salad. The Dana Girls would have to wait, suspended in time, until I next picked up my precious mystery book.

14

HOMECOMING

American Diamond 1969
Soldier
Army-tough, Vietnam-bound
Trudging, Collapsing, Suffering
Uncle Sam Needs You, Make Love Not War
Returning, Hoping, Reuniting
Vilified, Dejected
Outcast

Vietnam veterans hold a special place in my heart. Their treatment by the American people when they returned from combat in the 1960s and 70s was nothing less than immoral. Demonstrators, yelling and cursing, met them at the US airports when they landed, carrying signs that said, "Baby Killers" and "Make Love, Not War." These men had just served our country in hot, dirty, dangerous conditions and were returning to the safety and comfort of their homeland, or so they thought.

Most of these two million young men were drafted and did not choose to go to war. But fight they did, and the toll was tremendous in terms of injuries and deaths. For those fortunate enough to return home, the public reception could be devastating. More than one veteran patient of mine has told me that during their flight from overseas back to the States they were advised to change into their civvies—civilian clothes—in the airport restroom as soon as they landed. They were advised not to wear their uniforms in public, but they were often recognized as military nonetheless because of their short-cropped hair and tanned skin.

So, I love my Vietnam veteran patients, no matter how tough they may seem—wizened faces, tattoos, strong odor of tobacco, grey ponytails braided down their backs. Not all Vietnam veterans fit this picture, but enough do. Whether they do or not, I have made a pledge to treat all of them with an extra dose of respect and caring.

Mr. Keller—Petty Officer Keller—served in the Navy in the mid-1960s, both onboard a ship and on the ground in Vietnam as a supply clerk. Two decades later, he comes to see me in my clinic for a chronic cough. As we discuss his symptoms and go through his social and work history, he reveals to me that he is in the Navy's registries for both Shipboard Hazard and Agent Orange Exposure. Both of us know that the former may have exposed him to chemical and nuclear damage during shipboard drills. Agent Orange has been associated with many cancers, diabetes, and neuropathy, among other conditions. So here was a sailor who was drafted, served honorably for six years, and was unknowingly exposed to dangers far beyond those related to communism or the Viet Cong.

During his physical examination today, his heart and lung examination are both unremarkable, so I order a chest x-ray. And there it is: a left upper lobe mass. The lung specialist performs a bronchoscopy and takes samples, and not long after that, a diagnosis of squamous cell cancer growls back at me from the lab report.

When I tell Mr. Keller the news, he is stoic, accepting the hand life has dealt him. In the all-too-few months that follow, he receives chemotherapy for the inoperable tumor, and, as a result, becomes weak, dizzy, and bald. The Veterans Administration begins sending him a monthly stipend, because he had developed a condition associated with Agent Orange. It is, of course, little consolation.

"Dr. Camosy," he asks me one day, "did Agent Orange cause my lung cancer?"

While there is no definite way to know if AO was the cause or not, I tell him that it is a risk factor in his case.

While his smoking certainly is a risk factor as well, all service members who served in Vietnam are presumed by the VA to be exposed to Agent Orange and are automatically compensated for exposure if they develop lung cancer.

Mr. Ortega, another Vietnam veteran patient of mine, has been struggling with chronic neck and back pain since an injury during the war. His unit took incoming fire, and he was heavily wounded. He does not recall anything that occurred between a red flash and awakening in a hospital bed aboard the hospital ship *USS Sanctuary*. Urgent surgery saved his life, and to this day, he still carries shrapnel in his lumbar spine. We have been working together for several years to lessen his back pain, to allow him to do the things he enjoys around his house with his three grandchildren.

He tells me the all-too-familiar story. After returning from the war, he was called a warmonger. A few months later, after he was discharged from the military, Mr. Ortega attended college classes using the GI Bill, pursuing a degree in engineering. Even that experience, which should have been a positive one, he tells me today, filled him with anxiety because he felt he had to keep quiet about his military service. He pretended to be just another college student, while demonstrators picketed on the quad outside his classroom. He never told the students sitting next to him that he was an Army veteran.

Other Vietnam veteran patients have shown me a different type of lingering trauma. Some of them, because they were mistreated by the American public after their non-voluntary military service, are highly mistrusting of authority and formal organizations. A pneumonia patient of mine refused to be admitted to our local hospital because he did not trust hospitals. Another patient refused a flu shot from my nurse because the military had forced him to be immunized before going overseas.

Treating my Vietnam veteran patients with a bit of extra caring is rewarding to us both. I get to hear their stories, if they want to share them, and give them the thanks for their service that they did not receive when they first deserved it so many years ago.

15

VIOLATION

She sits on the ER gurney, and I on a stool beside her. Just below the edge of the curtain I see the shiny black shoes of the Marine Corps military police officer who is keeping watch. We are closed off from the rest of the world by a pale blue curtain and an unspeakable trauma.

My female patient has just been sexually assaulted on base.

With an unsettled heart, I review all that I must do in the next few minutes: call for a social worker, examine the patient, collect specimens for medical care and forensic evidence, and provide treatment. As with all things military, there is a formal standing operating procedure for me to follow. But the humanity of the situation puts a less procedural focus on the tasks ahead. Above all, I must act as healer for this poor woman, with kindness and gentleness at the top of my to-do list.

Moments before, the MP, who had a gruff voice but kind eyes, told me that the young woman was carrying her groceries home from the commissary in the early evening hours when the attack occurred. She was first struck across the face and then raped after she fell to the ground.

"It only took a few minutes," he told me, "then the perpetrator ran off. We are still searching for him."

Only a few minutes to change the rest of this woman's life, I thought. Everything about this moment feels dysphoric, as if an evil grey fog has enveloped us both.

Even words have lost their meaning. I cannot *welcome* her. I cannot say that I am *happy to meet her* today. I cannot even tell her that I will do my very best to *treat* her. She has been victimized in a violent way, and I cannot undo that as I would a bacterial infection. Words are inadequate, but I must try.

"Ms. Atwood, my name is Dr. Camosy, and I am so sorry that this has happened to you." I pause. "I promise to take care of you—you are safe here."

I take a deep breath, keenly aware of every inch of space between us and taking care not to touch her at this point. She nods slightly, but her downcast eyes do not move. Her green hospital gown, snapped closed at the back, is baggy on her slight frame. I know that her clothes have been taken as evidence. Her curly brown hair is disheveled, and there is a beefy-red swollen abraded area at her left jaw line. She fidgets with a tissue on her lap.

"Please let me know if you need anything," I tell her sympathetically. I feel she needs quiet and calm at this point, and I try to oblige. "I am waiting for the social worker to be with us while I check you over."

Just as I ask the nurse to get Ms. Atwood an ice pack for her face, the hospital social worker steps through the curtain and introduces herself.

"I am Leila, and I will stay with you this evening, Charlene."

Her voice is soothing. As the patient holds the ice to her jaw, I take a medical history, being careful not to rush. Speaking slowly and gently, I want her to know that I care about her wellbeing, not just about her answers to my questions. She tells me that she is single and that her only medical problem is intermittent asthma, which is not bothering her tonight. She takes the birth control pill, and she did have sex with her boyfriend last night. Her last menstrual period was one week ago, and she has never been pregnant.

As we talk, her eyes soften just a bit. By this time, the charge nurse has entered the bay with a forensic rape kit, which I will use to collect specimens to be used as evidence. I ask Charlene for permission to do an examination, hoping to myself that my exam will not cause her more physical or emotional torment. She assents, and I gently look over all of her skin, making careful chart notes of the bruises on her face and trunk. *This is the easy part,* I tell myself.

Following the protocol, I take fingernail scrapings and swabs of her mouth for gonorrhea culture and microscopic analysis for sperm. Each sample is labeled carefully and handed them off to the nurse who maintains a chain-of-custody paper. During this very clinical process, I do my best to balance Charlene's fragile medical and emotional needs with the need for precise collection of forensic evidence.

As our minutes together turn into a half-hour, Charlene begins to fidget less and looks up at me with eyes that are clearer.

"I sure could use a smoke."

"Charlene, if you can be strong," I respond, "I need to do a pelvic exam. Then we can take you outside for a cigarette. I know you are tired."

She nods again.

With Leila standing next to the head of the exam table, my nurse helps Charlene lie down and put her feet in the stirrups. Next, I tell her what I have told dozens of women before a pelvic exam, but today each word takes on a new meaning.

"I will be super gentle, Charlene, I promise. If anything I do is uncomfortable, let me know, and I will stop right away."

Before I insert the speculum, my nurse hands me a comb and plastic bag. I gently comb downward through the pubic hair to collect whatever falls into the bag—a few hairs, origin unknown. Adjusting the bright gooseneck lamp onto her vaginal opening, I make note of some moderate labial swelling and redness and the absence of lacerations. Apologizing to the patient, I gently insert a small-sized speculum as the social worker places her hand on Charlene's with a reassuring smile.

I thank God when I see that there is no sign of internal trauma. But a creamy liquid is present, and I again collect samples for culture and microscopy. The sample collecting continues—blood and urine for pregnancy testing and baseline infection status.

Finally, all the collections are complete, and I give Charlene an antibiotic shot. The social worker helps her into a wheelchair for a short ride to the ambulance entry area and a cigarette. I watch them talk as the smoke swirls around them. Charlene becomes a bit more animated, conversing with Leila and glancing somewhat warily at her surroundings. This is a conversation I must not interrupt.

When the two of them return to the emergency room, the MP with the kind eyes asks Charlene if she is up to speaking with a detective, and he invites the social worker to accompany them. I say goodbye and invite her to call me if she needs anything, anything at all. At that moment, I am feeling immensely inadequate. I know that there is nothing I can say or do to erase her pain, but I hope that my care today did not add to it.

I head to the staff coffee mess for a short break, feeling a sudden need to sit down, close my eyes, and squeeze out my emotional sponge. My heart is filled with inky puddles of Charlene's terror. As the greyness starts to dissipate, I wonder if it will ever leave me.

Perhaps I should not try to rid myself of the discomfiture, I hypothesize as I sip my coffee. I am a better physician for having cared for Charlene tonight. I hope that I am strong enough to carry her experience with me.

16

"THE THING WITH FEATHERS"

I always smile when I see Mr. Knowles's name on my clinic schedule. He is a cheerful man who never fails to ask me, with genuine concern, how I am doing. In his mid-sixties and a retired electrician, he and his wife of forty years have been coming to see me for years.

We have known for several months now that dear Mr. Knowles is dying from liver cancer, although it is more correct to say that he is living despite liver cancer.

He is a hospice patient and loves to remind me every time he comes into my clinic, in his slow Texas drawl, "My liver doctor told me that I had six months to live—and that was two years ago!"

And every time I love to tell him, "God must still have plans for you here!"

Today he comes in to see me with his wife, Bea. Together they fill me in on the latest goings-on with their grandchildren, going back and forth delightfully, interrupting each other and completing each other's sentences. He tells me today that he has been honest with his family about his younger days of alcohol abuse. His own father was a heavy drinker, so the younger Mr. Knowles encourages his loved ones not to drink alcohol, and, if they do, to be very careful.

Throughout our conversation, I note to myself that he looks thinner than last month, with a tinge more yellow to his skin. But his positive personality has never flagged.

"D' y'all know how my last lab test came out, Dr. Camosy? I really studied for it!"

I laugh out loud.

For years I have been managing his liver cirrhosis along with a local liver physician, and I still recall the day that his screening abdominal ultrasound first showed a suspicious mass. The specialist performed a biopsy the following week, and the diagnosis was hepatocellular carcinoma. The cancer had spread to his bones and lungs, giving Mr. Knowles an extremely poor prognosis.

So, today we discuss his medication for pain control and nausea and adjust his water-pill dose to deal with excess abdominal fluid from his diseased liver. The physical issues are more straightforward to deal with than the emotional ones, and I am careful to allow both Mr. and Mrs. Knowles time to express their thoughts and concerns. Several months ago, we carefully went through his wishes for end-of-life care.

Through it all, Mr. Knowles remains upbeat. His wife confirms that her husband has always looked at the positive side of life, for all the decades that they have been together. She and I agree that his cheerfulness has probably added weeks, months, even years, to his life, and we are, in turn, happy for his happiness.

"I wish that more of my patients had your cheery outlook, Mr. Knowles."

I think about the patient I saw earlier this same morning, who has no major medical conditions, but worries about every symptom he has, no matter how fleeting. To add to his woes, he never misses a chance to complain about some injustice he has suffered at the hands of his family and acquaintances.

"Well, doc," Mr. Knowles tells me, "I always think that bein' happy is a choice, just like gloominess is a choice. I wake up each day and hear that mockingbird singin' in the pecan tree outside my window, so I decide to be happy. Always have and always will."

I marvel at his down-home Texas wisdom. As a physician, I know that research has shown that the mental outlook of cancer patients is linked to their physical prognosis. Laughter and happiness increase white blood cell function to fight infection, decrease cortisol levels to lessen inflammation, and bring other health-promoting effects. When all is said and done, whether homespun wisdom or scientifically-proven data, the effects are spectacular to behold: a hopeful patient, a consoled family, and one grateful physician.

Mr. Knowles died in his home, peacefully and quietly, just like he lived. His wife and the hospice nurse were at his side. I hope that his wife remembers him whenever she hears a mockingbird sing its melodious song.

And thanks to Mr. Knowles, when I hear the Texas state bird high up in its tree home, I often think of Emily Dickinson's timeless poem from over a century ago.

> 'Hope' is the thing with feathers –
> That perches in the soul –
> And sings the tune without the words –
> And never stops – at all –

17

FIFTY-NINE

This day is unfolding routinely in my clinic. By mid-morning I have caught up with all my lab results and telephone triages, in between sips of coffee and seeing my scheduled patients. I go from exam room to exam room trying not to watch the clock too closely.

I walk into Room 3 to see Mrs. Greenwood, a thirty-four-year-old homemaker and part-time paralegal. She is on my schedule today for neck pain, or at least that is what she told my secretary when she called to make her appointment. As she and I settle in for our visit, I note that she bends forward on the chair, an aura of tension swirling around her.

"I have a few problems to discuss with you today," she announces, pulling a folded paper out of her purse.

As she does so, her right foot starts tapping on the floor.

This is not my first experience with The List. When a patient comes in with written documentation of multiple complaints, most physicians, myself included, cringe just a bit. It is not that we are unwilling or incapable of handling more than one issue at a visit. Time and thoroughness are the issues, and it is a sure bet that we will soon be behind schedule for the rest of the day.

I start by asking Mrs. Greenwood how many items are on her list. As it turns out, her description of "a few problems to discuss" is an outrageous understatement. She turns the paper over and scans to the bottom.

"Fifty-nine," she tells me in a matter-of-fact tone, in which I detect a challenge.

What strikes me at this point is not simply the raw number of complaints which she brings to me today, but the fact that she does not believe that this is unusual or abnormal. Fifty-nine. Fifty-nine! I briefly recall the patient I saw yesterday, who had three concerns. He started our appointment by apologizing to me for "being such a complainer."

"May I look at your paper?" I ask Mrs. Greenwood.

She hands me the slightly crumpled yellow legal-sized page, and I scan it.

The list is actually numbered down to 59 and contains a variety of subjective body-wide complaints that span the past ten years.

"Mrs. Greenwood," I begin, leaning toward her, "it looks here like you have really had a rough time, and

1. Dizzy when I watch TV
2. Right ankle pain
3. Nauseous for 8 months
4. Ears and lips tingle
5. Neck pain
6. Low back pain, getting worse
7. Very tired in the morning, hard to get out of bed
8. Heartburn at night
9. Feel feverish
10. Chest pain
11. Sometimes my ankles swell
12. Itchy neck, sometimes a rash, 6 years
13. . . .
14. . . .
. . .
. . .
. . .
. . .
58. Right eye twitches when I am tired
59. Trouble falling asleep

I want to help you with the items on this list. I'll bet that I am not the first doctor you have mentioned these concerns to, am I?"

"No one has been able to help me get rid of these problems, even after lots of tests." *Tap-tap-tap* goes her foot. Obviously very frustrated, she sits further forward to the edge of her chair. She is clearly looking to me to solve all the problems on her list today. *Tap-tap-tap.*

We scan her medical record together, and I see that she has come to see other providers in my group over the years. Three years ago, she came in with a list of twenty-five complaints. There have been multiple lab tests, two negative cardiac workups for chest pain, x-rays and MRIs of most of her joints, and several abdominal CT scans.

As we talk a bit more, I discover that she has been treated in the past for depression but stopped the medication because she "felt like a zombie" when taking it. After ensuring that she is not suicidal today, I try to explore her home and family situation a bit more. I ask her what her childhood was like. Each time she diverts the conversation back to The List.

Now more aggravated, she tells me, "The other doctors tried to blame it all on my depression and my weight, and I just know that it not the problem. Dr. Camosy, I know I am not crazy, and I am not making this up just to get attention. What can you do?"

Tap-tap-tap.

Now I am beginning to feel aggravated. My patient will not allow me to explore the layers beneath her listed symptoms, to look for a unifying social or psychological cause. She will not go there, and I wonder why.

As I listen to Mrs. Greenwood's words and their underlying emotion, my mind clicks through a differential list for multiple somatic complaints: hypochondriasis, malingering, somatization disorder. Settling on the latter, at least for now, I remember that it is a chronic condition characterized by multiple complaints with no physical findings and no cause to be found. I also remind myself that all her symptoms, all fifty-nine of them, are very real to her, just as real as if there *were* a physical cause. In addition, a positive relationship between the patient and physician is a huge part of healing.

Tap-tap-tap.

I push aside my sense of irritation and put a sympathetic smile on my face.

"I have several ideas, Mrs. Greenwood," I offer, "and I would like to see what you think of them."

I want her to know that I am taking The List very seriously.

So I present to her my own list of ideas to help her feel better. Let's prioritize the complaints, to see if one or two are the most important. Let's have her see my clinic counselor, since anyone with such problems would naturally be depressed by them all. And let's set up a monthly appointment, so we can work on her problems and get her feeling better together.

I notice that the room is silent; the tapping has stopped.

18

DESPERATION

Utter desperation ... de-sper ... *without hope.*

Empty, parched, destitute.

We have all experienced depression on a certain level and felt the psychic pain it can bring. Most of us, though, cannot fathom how hopelessness can become so encompassing it would drive a person to kill himself.

I think about Robin Williams, the beloved comedian and actor. How could a man who brought so much laughter to me and to others be so deeply troubled himself? I ponder the last few hours, minutes, seconds of his life. I cannot help myself. What was Robin feeling in those moments? Why did he feel that his life was not worth living? How deep must have been his pain! Did he think at all about the loved ones he would leave behind?

My questions become personal. How many of my patients put on a cheerful face for me and do not tell me of their troubled spirit?

My conclusion is that such desperation simply is not comprehensible to those of us who have never experienced that inky-dark night of the soul. Some measure of hope comes to me, though, in realizing that if I will but listen to my patients, each of whom I care about so very much, they can bring me closer to an understanding. My clinic exam room becomes a sanctum sanctorum; patients reveal to me inner thoughts that they have never verbalized, perhaps even never realized. For me, the healer, their sharing becomes a treasured gift, a grace, an honor. It can also be a call to action.

Be a caring and patient listener, I tell myself often throughout the bustle and haste. This self-reminder often pays off, as it does on this day. Mr. Ince is a fifty-two-year-old plumber whom I have known for a few years. He is married and basically healthy, taking medication only for gout and depression. His life has had its ups and downs, though, and I have been treating him with medication and supportive therapy for depression. Every few months we talk about what has been going on, and as he unfurls his life story to me, he appears genuinely pleased that I listen and care.

At our last visit, he revealed that his marriage was "crumbling" because he does not have a job.

"I sit around the house all day while my wife works, and she hates that," he admitted.

His grown son is a drug addict who, when he is not in jail, lives in a trailer on the rear part of their lot. Mr. Ince and I talked about his own lack of energy, his somnolence, and his feelings of inadequacy as a husband and a parent. Still, he declined my offers to refer him to a counselor, telling me that he prefers our conversations and my help. He has never been suicidal.

Until now.

On this particular day, he comes to my clinic for a routine follow-up appointment. My nurse takes his vital signs and talks to him to collect a brief history. As she leaves the exam room and hands me his chart, she tells me that Mr. Ince appears particularly depressed today. Indeed, when I enter the exam room, I note that our patient is indeed quieter than usual, eyes downcast. He is slumped in his chair, unshaven, and wearing a T-shirt that is frayed at the edges.

He still manages a "Hi, doc," when he sees me.

We shake hands and I settle into my chair, ready for an important conversation. I am not ready for what I hear next.

"Not a good week, doc," he tells me, his voice mellow, his eyes pooling up. A flow of words pours out as he confides in me. "My wife finally left me. I have been expecting this for a long time, but I never really thought that she would do it." He pauses as if to underscore this last point. "Now that she is gone, I can't imagine life without her. My heart hurts, my breathing hurts, it even hurts me to keep my eyes open to look at you now. Everything has gone to hell, and I know it will never stop."

Shifting in his chair, he continues. "Yesterday, I could not take the pain any longer, so I decided to do what my father did." His voice suddenly sounds quieter, far away. "He killed himself when I was twelve—hanged himself in our garage. Don't be shocked, Dr. Camosy, at what I am going to tell you now. Yesterday morning, I got a rope and threw it over our garage ceiling rafter."

I hold my own breath reflexively.

"But I couldn't go through with it. So I went into our bathroom and took out all our pill bottles, poured the pills into a bowl. I thought this would be an easier way to go, but I was too much of a coward to take them. But I have a gun, a 45. I got it out, loaded it, put it on the kitchen table. Something made me call my wife to tell her what I had done. She talked me out of using the gun."

We sit quietly for a moment. In an effort to help us both see some positives in his life, I ask him what stopped him from killing himself yesterday, three times no less. He closed his eyes and thought for a moment. His faith in God and his religion tell him that it would be wrong, he responded, and that he would go to hell. Plus, he still fosters some hope that he can "patch things up" with his wife.

"I will be hopeful along with you, Mr. Ince. That's double the hope. I know we can get you feeling better."

We talk for a few minutes more, as I silently develop my plan.

He clearly needs admission to the hospital for suicidal ideation with a well-developed intent and plan, and thankfully he does not argue with me when I tell him this. A few safety checks are in order, so I ask him if he has any weapons on him now. He does not. In addition, I know that my clinic exam rooms contain no scalpels, needles, scissors, or anything else that could be used for harm.

Leaving the exam room door open, I go to the front desk to ask my secretary to call 9-1-1 and my nurse to sit with Mr. Ince. His triple-suicide plan grabs my full attention that day, as does his family history of paternal suicide. In the back of my mind, I wonder if yesterday's events were all a marital kabuki-dance designed to get the attention of his wife. I do know that his psychic distress is real, and that we can give him the help he needs.

After spending a week on the psychiatric ward under the care of mental health specialists, Mr. Ince returns home, with close follow-up by a psychologist and suicide prevention social worker. His wife does go on to divorce him, and he remains depressed each time I see him, but not suicidal. The best I can offer him is a listening ear, hopeful words, and occasional advice. This seems to be enough for him.

19

SHOW-AND-TELL

My nervous fingers curled over the edge of the hard, wooden desk. *It's almost my turn. One, two, three more kids in front of me.* The anticipation was churning my insides.

Joey proudly showed a black and green shimmery feather, its needlelike sides—barbules, he told us—zipping open and closed with two sweeps of his fingers. Next came Carol, holding up a solitary butterfly wing, crisp and tangerine-colored and pretty, but at the same time, sad in its incompleteness.

What happened to the rest of the butterfly? I wondered as I waited my turn.

Mrs. Bell's weekly show-and-tell rituals, steeped in the smell of chalkboard dust and pencil shavings, always focused our young third-grade brains on nature. The objects, which at first seemed to belong only to us after we picked them up off the grass (*finders, keepers!*) became part of a larger wonder-filled universe once she began to talk. She expertly wove together facts about the natural world—the science, the intricacy, the beauty. Each item had a place in the ecosystem and in the timeline of the landscape. The found object, she told us, actually belonged to no one and to everyone.

The classroom experience of show-and-tell has been ubiquitous in America for decades. There is even an adult version called "found art," in which the artist displays a collage of objects that were discovered on the ground, in closets, in pockets, wherever. We show off interesting items that we have found in order to share the wonderment. This desire for connectivity is part of our human nature.

Long before the 1910 Flexner Report outlined the basic principles of modern medical education, even long before the existence of medical schools to teach aspiring physicians, the art and science of medicine were passed along through show-and-tell moments such as Mrs. Bell's lessons. For those of us who truly enjoy the healthcare profession, the opportunity to demonstrate to others human pathophysiology in its purest form brings its own energy to the clinical setting.

"Dr. Camosy, we need you in Room 3," comes an urgent request from my nurse.

I enter the exam room and do not recognize the patient sitting on the exam table, a red bandana loosely wrapped around both of his eyes.

A man standing next to him tells me, "We were building the gas station next door, and a nail he was hammering flew into his eye!"

I begin to untie the bandana, expecting to find a corneal abrasion, or perhaps a laceration to his eyelid. As the cloth drops, the three of us see a half-inch of nail protruding from his left eye, from the sclera to be precise. The nail has penetrated the white of his eye, just three millimeters from the more delicate tissues of his cornea, iris, and lens.

As I look at his injured eye, I note that he is looking back at me and scanning my face for a reaction.

"Okay, we have some work to do here before I can send you off to the eye specialist," I begin. "Thankfully, it looks like the nail missed the vision part of your eye." I realize that this uncommon clinical finding should be shared with all of my clinic staff, and I delve into show-and-tell mode. "Everyone should know how to deal with a penetrating eye injury. Let's get them all in here."

As the clinic nurses and physician assistant enter to see what all the fuss is, I explain that we must leave the nail in place, protect the eye from any further damage, and prevent the nail from moving. Contrary to any medical instinct, I must not pull out the nail; this would likely cause more damage, such as extrusion of globe contents.

I ask for a paper drinking cup. Following directions that I have only read about in a medical textbook, I use the bandage scissors in my lab coat pocket to cut six one-inch slits along the open edge of the cup. Next, I splay open each tab and tape the cup to his face, covering the eye and the protruding nail. I conclude my real-life performance art.

"Now he is ready to go to the ER."

One of the nurses murmurs, "That was really cool," as she heads to the phone to call for a transport ambulance.

In my third-grade classroom, as James returned to his desk next to mine, I arose and smoothed down my plaid skirt with one hand. I walked self-consciously to the front of the room and stood next to Mrs. Bell's desk. I held up my treasure, a pinecone that had been nestled under a tree a short distance from our house. Just larger than my closed fist, its chocolate-brown spiked nubs were spread open as if to say, "Look at me!"

"This is my pinecone—it did not look like this when I picked it up yesterday," I said timidly to the class, as I touched the individual spikes and saw the indentations on my finger. "It was smaller and wet and all closed up tight." The budding scientist in me proffered an explanation, derived from our home set of Britannica encyclopedias. "When the weather is warm and dry, the pinecone opens up to let its seeds out, so they can spread around and grow more pine trees."

I swept my arms up and open, becoming a pine tree, and smiled at the grandiosity of it all. Mrs. Bell nodded.

20

EEYORE

Eeyore, or rather a patient who reminds us of Eeyore, comes in to our clinic every couple of months. Winnie-the-Pooh's grumpy grey donkey friend lives in Eeyore's Gloomy Place in the Hundred Acres Woods and is in a perpetually cranky mood. He also has a habit of losing his tail, and when his friends fix him up with a new one, he comments morosely, "Most likely lose it again, anyway." He is a donkey of few words.

And so, my patient Mr. Taylor shuffles almost aimlessly into the clinic, his head lowered, his voice quiet and deep. As he checks in at the window, "Thanks for noticin' me," the front desk secretary puts on her brightest smile and tries without success to cheer him up. "If it is a good morning, which I doubt."

The first time I met him in my clinic, I remember sensing a pervasive sadness ... ennui ... was it derision? Every question I posed, every comment I made, was met with a negative comment and a downward curl of his lips. We went through his social and medical history, review of systems, and physical examination and then reviewed his blood work results. Mr. Taylor had emphysema, and although he had quit smoking long ago, he continued to have shortness of breath. As I tried to make a therapeutic plan with him, my caring and concern was met with disapproval at each step.

"I've tried that; it doesn't work."

"My neighbor told me that is a dangerous drug"

"That will never help me."

Mr. Taylor and I were developing a patient-physician relationship, to be sure, but it seemed inverse, or converse, or just plain gloomy.

Through it all, as I worked to fashion a new tail for this ersatz Eeyore, I resisted the invisible force pulling me into his dour and complaint-filled world. As the visit drew to a close, the dis-ease continued. I felt nothing of the usual connection I make with new patients—no mutual interests, no desire to move toward healing and better health.

"Is there anything else?" I asked him.

He had no further concerns. "Could be worse. Not sure how, but it could be."

In my career, I have dealt with many a patient like Mr. Taylor. Medical textbooks are filled with chapters on "dealing with the difficult patient," or "managing the angry patient." After Mr. Taylor left the clinic on that first day, I took some extra time to educate my clinic staff on the importance of providing positivity to counterbalance his negativity,

"Think of protons and electrons," I told them.

When faced with such a patient, I listen with real and obvious interest to what he says, and I slow down to be in the moment with him. And I smile more. The smile approach has basis in research; if one is feeling stressed or sad, the mere act of forming your facial muscles into a smile (yes, a fake smile) acts on your body's neurotransmitters to cause a sense of happiness. It works, this smile in reverse.

Less than a week after this first visit, Mr. Taylor called my nurse with multiple complaints about my care. I had not ordered a home blood pressure monitor. I did not address the very mildly abnormal calcium on his lab report. Six months is too long for him to wait for the next appointment.

So this went on for a year or so, visit after morose visit, followed by complaint phone calls to my nurse. At each clinic visit, I addressed whatever concerns Mr. Taylor voiced to me and tried to understand the thoughts and experiences that drove his personality. I went so far as to offer him a new physician, which he declined. It became clear that he used this anti-therapeutic modus operandi with all his physicians. Despite his complaints to my nurse, he did not actually feel my care was substandard. He enjoyed grumbling. Eeyore will be Eeyore. "Nothing to do ... and no hope of things getting better."

After about a year, we settled into a routine, and the telephone complaints to my nurse stopped. He still has a perpetually down-turned mouth, and he still speaks in mournful phrases, but I have noticed a softening in his demeanor. It is as if we have passed some sort of test he has laid out for his caregivers. If I and my staff could deal with his gloominess and show him that we will not stop caring, then he will let us fashion him a new tail, so to speak. This is to be our reward. "It is an awful nice tail, Kanga. Much nicer than the rest of me."

As a healer, I would like to think that our smiles and kind words, even if never acknowledged, provide Mr. Taylor some measure of comfort. Maybe not. But it is the right thing for us to do, and it keeps us all from joining him in Eeyore's Gloomy Place.

21

"DOIN' JES' FINE"

As I open the door to see my next patient, I feel myself being pushed backward, tipping on my heels. In less than a second, less than four inches of the door opening, the odor hits me like a two-by-four. After a moment of surprise, I advance slowly into the room while the invisible force swirls around the room in miasmic fashion. I try my best to smile.

Until this moment, I have never experienced smell as a physical entity. Sure, my high-school physiology teacher taught us that an odor is physical matter, unseen airborne molecules that enter our nasal passages and interact with olfactory nerve endings deep within the nose. And in college we learned that the olfactory nerve transmits exquisitely sensitive and specific signals from the ethmoid bone's cribiform plate to the forebrain. They are the body's only nerve cells that are in direct contact with the air. I'll say.

"Good afternoon, Mr. Jones. It's nice to see you today," I lie.

Sitting on the end of the exam table, slightly slumped and unshaven, he looks every bit of his sixty-seven years. He is emitting the most noxious smell of body odor, dirt, and tobacco. His jeans are faded and worn, his plaid shirt frayed at the sleeve edges. As we start to talk, my nose and throat are burning, and my eyes feel irritated. I feel rent in two: *I have to get out of here*, screams my body. *You must care for this patient*, argues my mind. Confidentiality of our conversation prevents me from re-opening the door for some relief.

Mr. Jones is here today for a routine follow-up of his hypertension and osteoarthritis, which is simple enough. A very brief review of systems reveals no chest pain, no shortness of breath, no edema. *I can't take this much longer.* Before I begin my physical examination, I visually scan his scalp and skin for scabies or head lice: negative. My eyes start to water, and a wave of nausea rises up.

Retreating to the stool in the farthest corner of the exam room, I begin a review of his social history. It must be done, I know, even though my body is still fighting me. *How soon can I get this over with?* He does not notice my discomfort.

"Where are you living now, Mr. Jones?"

"I got me a new trailer now, just outta town. A really nice one."

He goes on to describe the area of the North Carolina back country that he calls home. His cognition is intact, and he shows no signs of depression or substance abuse.

We talk a bit more, and I ask if his new trailer has electricity (yes) and running water (no). But he assures me that the trailer park has public bathroom facilities.

"That sounds difficult," I venture.

"Naw, it be fine with me. I keeps to myself. I likes to watch the TV."

With a few more well-targeted questions, I reassure myself that his basic needs are being met, but I want to help him nonetheless. I offer to have a social worker call him. "Just to see if there are some programs in your area that you might like."

"Doc, I really be doin' jes' fine on my own. 'Sides, my ex-wife comes over from time to time to help me clean, and she brings me a casserole." He pauses. "I don' need no charity."

"Fair enough," I tell him as I stand up and open the door. "Can I have my nurse give you a flu shot today? It is really important."

Andrea uses four alcohol pads to clean the layers of dirt off a circle of his upper arm and gives him the injection. Mr. Jones and I say a friendly farewell, and he agrees to schedule another appointment with me in six months. Down the hallway he and his olfactory emissions travel, God bless him, out the clinic door and home to his country trailer world, where he has everything that he needs. But the odor remains in the exam room. All the citrus room spray in the world will not eradicate it today.

As I make my way down the hallway back to my office, I take in a deep breath. The odor is still present, and thoughts of Mr. Jones linger with me as well. I know that he would qualify for assistance—food stamps, at least—but he chooses to live independently, autonomously, for whatever his reasons. Is it pride or a kindness of spirit that does not want to trouble others, or perhaps agoraphobia or paranoia? Answers may lie ahead as we get to know each other better, but for now he needs a physician who will respect his autonomy and his lifestyle decisions.

Everyone wants to be listened to, understood, and respected. Sometimes my patients make decisions that do not seem logical to me. They may choose *not* to follow my recommendation: the annual flu shot ("it always makes me sick"), a screening mammogram ("that radiation causes breast cancer"), a medication for hypertension ("I do not like to take pills"). These distinct patient perceptions can sometimes be changed after a discussion with me, their physician and health advisor, but sometimes they cannot. If I know that my patient is a mentally competent adult who can verbalize to me that they understand the ramifications of their decision, then I swallow my ego and abandon my righting-reflex. We agree to disagree. By respecting my patient's autonomy, the therapeutic bond between us grows stronger.

22

SNAPSHOT

Incoming!

Run for cover!

Where's Sarge?

Early in my career, I had the privilege of caring for a handful of World War I veterans, who were very old at the time. In contrast, I was young and shy. Pursuing a career in medicine took all my energy, and I did not delve into my patients' military histories. I was looking forward, not backward. Alas.

Since then, I have learned that combat veterans are interesting people. I try to make time in my busy clinic day to ask my patients who are World War II veterans about their service days. It takes just a few minutes, and sometimes it occurs to me that we should be talking about things medical, but we can do that in a minute. So I sit back and listen to firsthand accounts of D-Day, the Battle of the Bulge, and the postwar Berlin airlift. Of patriotic men who lied about their ages to get into the military. The writer in me encourages them to document their experiences for their children, even if they do not fancy themselves to be writers. I mention that I wish my father had kept a record of some of his military experiences before he died.

I am truly saddened to be seeing fewer and fewer World War II veterans. These were really great men, who stood up when I entered the clinic exam room, no matter how long it took them with their weak knees.

My father, an Air Force forward air control pilot in Vietnam, never spoke to us about the horrors of combat after he returned. Instead, he told us about the children in the Vietnamese orphanage where he volunteered and showed us photos he had taken with his Polaroid Instamatic. I saw thin, smiling, dark-haired children, in bright colored yet worn-looking clothes. Many were barefoot. Looking back now, I am sure that my father's point with these stories was to show us the good that can come out of evil. He was encouraging us to be caring individuals and to be grateful for our family, home, food, and clothing.

When he returned from Vietnam, Dad looked like the same person, just more tanned. But his gentle spirit had been traumatized by the horrors of war, as has happened to soldiers for thousands of years. Thankfully for him, his distress lasted only a few months. He startled more easily when one of us walked up behind him, and I recall the nighttime quiet of our house pierced by his occasional yelling during his sleep. I did not realize it until many, many years later, but my father had PTSD, posttraumatic stress disorder.

In my career as a physician, I have cared for many combat veterans—from my active duty time in Florida, California, and North and South Carolina to my civilian life in Texas. I wanted to know how to diagnose and treat these brave men and women, so I began to read about PTSD. What I learned can be boiled down to these axioms, three nesting circles within circles:

1. Ask every patient if they are a military veteran.

2. Ask every military veteran if they saw combat.

3. Ask every combat veteran about symptoms of PTSD.

I sit in the exam room with Mr. Grunwald and his wife today, and the clinic visit begins as a typical one. He is a seventy-nine-year-old man, here for a follow-up of his hypertension and diabetes.

As usual for our visits, he has no complaints for me today, and I ask him offhandedly, "You served in the Army, right? What did you do in the military?"

Almost as rote, since I am sure he has been asked this question dozens of times, he answers, "I served in France for almost eighteen months during World War II. Artillery." He pauses, looks at his wife, and then back to me. When he sees that I am interested, he continues in a more solemn tone. "I still think about it a lot. It was cold as all get-out, and we would go for weeks without a warm meal, me and my buddy Nate. Nate."

Another pause, this one longer. I say nothing, not daring even to move.

"We were in a foxhole together when Nate took an incoming round straight on." Tears well up in Mr. Grunwald's eyes as he continues to recount with surprising clarity the events of forty years earlier. "It could have been me. It *should* have been me. Nate had a wife and new baby at home. I had no one." His voice drifts off. "It should have been me."

I am struck by the freshness of his tearful telling, as if it had occurred last week rather than decades ago. I also feel a sense of gratitude that he has chosen to share this painful, well-guarded episode of his life with me. But Mr. Grunwald's story is not done.

Again looking to his wife for comfort, he nods and allows her to continue his story for him.

"He still has nightmares about it. He relives it in his dreams, thrashes about in bed, and then wakes up in a sweat."

These nightmares occur several times a month. How very powerful a traumatic experience can be on the human spirit, that it continues to take its toll forty years later.

When I was trying to learn more about combat PTSD, the three symptom clusters from the Diagnostic & Statistical Manual of Mental Disorders organized themselves in my brain into a mnemonic: WAR.

Watchfulness, irritability

Avoidance of people and situations

Reliving the combat experience through nightmares or flashbacks

Listening to my PTSD patients over the years has shown me their symptoms in a very real way.

"I keep my shotgun loaded by the front door."

"I have a snapshot flash in front of my eyes, over and over, of the soldier with his arms blown off. I can't get it out of my memory."

"I never drive on freeways anymore. The bridge underpasses make me think of the bridge with the IED that exploded on us."

"I always feel like there is someone behind me, following me."

"I broke my wife's wrist in bed last year with my thrashing about."

"If I pass by a Vietnamese restaurant, I can't tell you how sick the smell of the food makes me."

"My job was to protect my lieutenant—and I failed her. I wish I had died instead."

"My third wife just left me because she could not take my angry outbursts. She begged me to get help; I wish I had listened to her."

"I was in charge of burying the civilians—the women and children—who had been killed. They were just innocent people. I cannot get that smell out of my mind."

So, although the topic may be an unpleasant one for the veteran and for the physician, it should be broached, so that the veteran, who may have suffered for a long time in silence, can be offered help for PTSD symptoms.

Then the question becomes *how does a family physician help the veteran with PTSD symptoms?*

"Mr. Grunwald," I tell my elderly patient sympathetically, "it sounds as if you are still suffering aftereffects from your service in the war. A lot of my patients who have been in combat tell me of similar thoughts, and I really want you to know that it is a rather normal reaction to a terribly violent situation. Some of my patients ask me if they are 'crazy,' (I make air quotes here), but they are not, and you are not.

"You may have PTSD," I continue, "which we can help you with. Counseling and medication are often effective in lessening and, in many cases, halting the symptoms. If you are interested, I can get you some help."

Most of my patients will accept my offer of help, if not initially, then at a later visit. Thankfully, Mr. Grunwald agrees to see a counselor.

But some veterans do not. For them, the same independence and strength of ego that brought them into the military isolate them after they leave active duty. They will not look to others for help or even admit to having a problem.

Mr. Ureste is a sixty-two-year-old Vietnam veteran on his fourth marriage. Grey ponytail down his back, he is irascible and tough as steel by his own admission.

During my W-A-R questions, he admits to me, "I get angry a lot. My wife tries to calm me down."

He avoids leaving the house, because traffic and crowds make him even more irritable, and he has frequent nightmares about his experiences on the rice paddy battlefields of Vietnam. As our conversation unfolds, Mr. Ureste does not agree that he may have PTSD.

"Nah, I just have a problem with my temper." He is not interested in my offer of help. I leave the option open, though, if he ever changes his mind. Cynically I think that perhaps he will call when his fourth wife leaves him.

My conversation with Mr. Ureste needed to take place nonetheless, as it does between every combat veteran and their physician.

I've got your six!

23

LESSONS LEARNED

I would rather you not read this chapter. No one enjoys reliving their mistakes, lapses in clinical judgment, or errors. Unlike many other professions, when a physician makes a mistake, the result can be disastrous. So, here we go.

Mrs. Knaus was a thirty-five-year-old woman who was *not* my patient. This last tiny fact became the crux of an error on my part, which occurred over twenty years ago. In the days before strict enforcement of patient privacy laws, I received a phone call from a friend, a mental health counselor. He was treating Mrs. Knaus for depression and anxiety and suspected that she was either lying or delusional about having advanced-stage cancer. The counselor asked if I would call her primary physician, also a friend of mine, to ask if she had cancer or not. Without much thought, I placed the call, only to learn that the patient did not have cancer.

I called back the counselor to inform him of his patient's prevarication. Shortly thereafter the patient mailed a letter of complaint to my director outlining my inappropriate breach of her right to confidentiality. She was correct, of course. Because I was not a member of her treatment team, I had broken the rules. I received a counseling session and a reprimand letter from the clinic director. Lesson learned.

During another busy clinic day, I see Robby, a rambunctious seven-year-old, for an earache and fever. I have seen him several times before and notated in his chart that he was allergic to penicillin. But on this day, my pen gets ahead of my brain, and I hand his mother a written prescription for amoxicillin, a form of penicillin, to treat his otitis. I advise her to call me in a few days if he is not better. After they leave the office, I write up the progress note and notice my error. A mad dash to the telephone corrects the situation. I tell Robby's mother not to fill the prescription, and then I speak with the pharmacist to give a verbal order for another antibiotic. We avert a potential disaster.

My continuous hope regarding my medical errors has always been two-fold: that I catch them early enough to correct the situation before the patient is harmed and that I learn a valuable lesson so as not to repeat that same mistake. I now check twice for allergies before I prescribe any medication and write the patient's medical allergies on the top of every written prescription. Lesson learned.

It is a wonder that we physicians do not miss more diagnoses than we do in the course of a busy hospital or clinic day. My mind flashes back in time to a handful of missed diagnoses—those that I know about, anyway.

There was the toddler whose mother told me his urine was dark and smelled sweet, so I evaluated him for diabetes. After my negative workup, the mother took him to a specialist who diagnosed maple-syrup urine disease, a relatively rare congenital disease that I have never again seen in my career.

I recall the overweight teenage girl with headaches, whom I evaluated in the clinic and diagnosed as probable tension headaches. The following week she developed blurry vision, and an eye doctor diagnosed pseudotumor cerebri. This is a benign fatty tumor behind the eye that is more common in overweight people and can regress with time. To this day, I wonder if I missed an abnormal eye exam and am extra careful with my headache patients. Lesson learned.

Human nature being what it is, we all make mistakes, major ones sometimes and little ones often. To counterbalance my perfectionist tendency, my personal technique is to do my best to ensure that every patient knows that I truly care about them and am doing my best to provide them with high-quality medical care. A strong therapeutic relationship covers a lot of missed diagnoses, misread x-rays, and erroneous prescriptions by making them understandable to the patient and by permitting me not to be excessively hard on myself.

24

DEAR DR. CAMOSY

Dear Dr. Camosy,

I know you are very busy and I have a lot I want to tell you, so I thought I would write you this letter. My life finanshuly has got worse, and I don't know how I am going to make ends meet. Really, you can't do nothing about it, I know, but you should know what is going on, since you are my doctor.

My dissability clame been denied, they say I will not get anything more than what I am getting now to help me out. So, I just get my work penshin, $360 each month, and my dissability $1240 a month. Since this is not enough, and since the goverment will not give me any more, I have decided to stop taking all my pills. This is what you need to know, as my doctor. I have to pay my rent and lectric bills, you know. I need a roof over my head. My landlord lets me be a few days late with the rent, but really I do not know how long that will last.

I can't afford all the pills for my preshure and diabetes and artritis. Since I do not know what damage this will cause to me, to stop the pills, we will just have to wait and see. Purhaps I will die, but there is no other choice, without the money. I do not want it this way, but a person has to eat, right?

Also, my family can't help me, they don't have no money neither. My son just had a new baby, and they are staying with his mother-in-law, just for a while, so he can look for a job. He tells me he wants to help me some day, but just not now.

This is what I want you to know.

Not everyone can be as blessed as the reader of this letter.

Your patient,

Laureen Blumenthal

I slowly put down my coffee mug and lean back in my chair, letting the rumpled yellow page fall to my desk. My eyes closed, I try to picture her writing this heartfelt letter to me in her home, or is it an apartment or a trailer? I pick it up again and re-read the sprawling printed words, deeply pressed onto the page by her pen, and try to focus my unsettled thoughts. She has written to tell me about her financial problems, but my eyes linger selfishly, almost angrily, on the last line. It is an unveiled assumption that I have had an easy path to fortune and riches. She knows nothing about my life, I tell myself. How dare she think that she does? Class envy is alive and well on the pages of this letter, and I am not so naive as to think that she is my only patient with such ideology.

My thoughts quickly soften. I know little about her life as well; I certainly had no idea that she was having financial difficulty. She has come to see me in my office a few times over the past year, for high blood pressure, diabetes, and chronic back pain, for which she is disabled. We have talked convivially, and I recall that we discussed the German origin of her last name—"flower valley" she told me. She was too proud, I now imagine, to tell me that she could not afford the medications that I was prescribing. I make a mental note, a course correction, to be more careful with my patients, not to act too busy to listen to their problems. I should ask them more often if there will be any problem paying for their medications.

Ms. Blumenthal's letter is crying out with desperation, and I resolve to assist her. Our clinic social worker contacts her the next day, and then reports to me that she was able to provide our patient with several community resources. As it turns out, my patient did not have to stop taking her medications, and she continues to come to our clinic for care.

She still struggles with her budget but has appealed her disability claim all the way up to her US congress-man, who is working on her behalf.

So, now she has more people advocating for her than before she wrote the letter, including a physician who still has to remind herself, from time to time, to be sure that all her patients feel that their doctor is listening to them.

25

BROKEN

"How can I help you today?"

I wonder how many hundreds of times I have asked this question to my patients.

We physicians would like to help all our patients; we want all our encounters to be positive and therapeutic. After all, we chose to spend our life's work as healers. But sometimes this bejeweled ideal is not meant to be.

Miss Reynaldo comes to my clinic one afternoon for an annual visit. I do not know her particularly well, but after reviewing her chart, I remember that she is fifty-two years old and divorced, an executive with a local advertising company. She has come to the office twice in the past for acute issues, and those visits flowed smoothly.

Today she is sitting in the exam room chair as I enter, looking over a day planner. She looks up, and I notice that her pale blue skirt-suit is neatly pressed and that her brown hair is starting to show grey at her temples. We greet each other and make small talk; no sign of a problem yet.

As we talk further and delve into her medical history, she tells me that her gynecologist has been prescribing estrogen and progesterone pills. I ask how long she has been on these medications (seven years) and when her last mammogram was (here comes the problem).

"Actually, Dr. Camosy, that is why I am here," she states in a definitive tone. "I need you to refill my estrogen pills today." An edge starts to creep into her voice, and she sits forward in her chair. "If I do not take them, I get hot flashes. But Dr. Harper, my gynecologist, will not refill them anymore. She has a thing about mammograms and will not stop pushing me to get one."

I put down my pen. "I tend to agree," I tell my patient. "Research studies have shown an increased risk of breast cancer, also stroke and heart attack, in women who have been on estrogens. And the longer you have been on them the higher the risk. I would really like to order you a mammogram today, Miss Reynaldo."

My scientific approach has no effect. I am surprised at the change in her demeanor, as she becomes irritated, then argumentative.

"You doctors are all alike. I do plenty of reading. I know that there is radiation in those mammograms, radiation that causes breast cancer. There is no way I will have another mammogram."

I start to reassure her of the safety of mammograms, but she cuts me off.

"I know my rights, and you cannot deprive me of a medication that I have been taking for seven years. I am *not* getting a mammogram, and you *will* prescribe my estrogen today."

Her demand is so uncompromising that I wonder whom she is accustomed to bossing around like this. She clearly is experienced at it.

"Miss Reynaldo," I say calmly, in an attempt to offset her angry tone, "I have to practice medicine as I feel is the best for my patients. It simply is not safe for me to prescribe you estrogen without a mammogram. So, now you have had two doctors give you the very same advice."

The uncomfortable back and forth continues several minutes, and the agitation in her voice rises even more. We are not having a productive patient-doctor discussion, not sharing ideas and opinions as two logical people would do. She will not waver from her *idée fixe*, her notion that mammograms cause breast cancer. She begins to stir up the dust of prior physician problems she has had. Dr. X gave her a medication that caused her peripheral neuropathy. Dr. Y only wanted her money, so he ordered blood test after blood test.

She returns to the estrogen issue. "You're just like them all, lady. You do not care about your patients, just about money. Let me tell you: you *will* give me the prescription today, or I will see you in court!"

I knew several minutes ago that our therapeutic relationship was broken, but this clinches it. The lack of connection between us causes me to wonder if she has ever experienced a healthy relationship with a physician. What I do know with certainty is that when a patient threatens to sue me, I will no longer be their physician.

"I can see that you do not have faith in my ability to treat you," I tell her.

Her blank stare belies the vitriol she has just expressed.

"Even more than that, when a patient threatens to sue me, I choose to stop being their doctor. I cannot treat you today or in the future, Miss Reynaldo, knowing that you will sue me if I do not do what you want."

As she stands silently to leave the exam room, I offer to write down the names of a few other physicians in the area for her, but she is not listening. Out the door she goes, most likely to start and break yet another doctor-patient relationship.

26

DR. TORTOISE AND DR. HARE

Slow down and enjoy your patients, I remind myself early one afternoon.

The morning was busy, chock-full of patients with a variety of reasons for coming to see me. In typical primary care fashion, I addressed bronchitis, diabetes, peripheral vascular disease, an ankle sprain, and anxiety. Neither my nurse nor I got a lunch break, so we quickly wrote our chart notes as we nibbled on sandwiches.

Slow down!

Responding to my self-administered advice, I enter the exam room to greet my first afternoon patient with what I hope is a relaxed smile. I shake his hand as we greet each other with a degree of familiarity. His eyes are friendly.

"It is nice to see you again, Mr. Sanchez," I say, placing my pen and clipboard on the counter next to the computer and turning toward him. I choose the arm chair rather than the rolling stool and settle in. "How are you doing today?"

Even after thirty years of practice, too often I find myself cranking out appointments and computerized notes in a methodical, time-efficient pattern. *Cling-clang-cling-clang* goes this doctor-machine. The clock on the wall is my task-master. *Room 1. Room 2. Room 1. Room ...*

Then it hits me once again.

Slow down and enjoy your patients!

I take a deep breath, calmness descends upon me, and I become the physician I like to be. In my slower mode, "slow medicine," as some call it, I learn things that I never would have otherwise about my patients, my precious patients. Some twenty years ago, when I was struck by this epiphany—and it was nothing less than that—I took off my wristwatch, stashed it in a drawer at home, and have never worn it again. No more glancing at the time while talking to a patient.

Today Mr. Sanchez mentions that he plans to visit his son in Tennessee next month. With pride in his voice, he tells me that he bought an RV last year with his savings from quitting smoking. He has not seen his grandchildren in a few years, and his son needs some fatherly encouragement for his new job.

Twelve-year-old Angie wants to change from playing the soprano recorder to the bass in the school ensemble, but her mother is concerned that it would be too difficult with her asthma. "It takes a lot more air to play the bass," Angie tells me, "but I really want to do it!" I encourage her and reassure her mother.

Knowing that I served in the Navy, Mr. Richards tells me that a national news reporter recently interviewed his buddy, a ninety-two-year-old Navy veteran, for a story on D-Day and his role onboard ship that day. My patient gives me the internet link to the story. Would he have done that, I wonder, if I had been in my hurry-up-and-stay-on-schedule mode?

More importantly, when I slow down to listen carefully, my patients reveal secret parts of their lives to me, feelings and experiences that, through the act of sharing, strengthen the therapeutic relationship between us.

Mr. Chavez tells me softly that he is afraid his wife will leave him soon because of his grumpy mood and his gambling online. If we had just focused on the reason for today's appointment, his shoulder pain, I would not have uncovered his depression, gambling addiction, and marital discord. But he felt free to mention his heartache because I sat with him and was not rushed.

A two-month well-baby check brings in Mrs. Blanchard and little Ellie. As we talk, *really* talk, she reveals to me that she cries much of the day while her husband is at work. She tosses and worries in bed at night. This new mother believes that she should feel delighted about her baby, but she does not. As a result, she thinks that she is "a bad mom." I am the first person, she tearfully tells me, who has listened to her and whom she can trust with this delicate information.

Ms. Eckert was just kicked out of her elderly mother's house and has no place to live. They have never gotten along well, and the daughter now feels that no one in her family appreciates all she did for her mother. She has no friends or family to turn to for help.

A slower-paced and relaxed mode of practicing medicine allows me to learn more about my patients, to be sure, and to become a better diagnostician and healer as a result. So, for those healthcare administrators who measure cost versus outcomes, such intentional slowness can actually be an improvement in efficiency. The tortoise beat the hare in their race, after all.

Equally important, slow medicine reflects the type of physician—the type of person—that I am constantly striving to be, even after decades of practice. The passion and goals that I started out with as a twenty-year-old medical student have not been extinguished, but they can be pushed aside during a very busy day.

I re-kindle them with two simple words: *Slow down!*

27

MY OWN FABLES

As the mighty lion slept, a tiny mouse began running from his head to his tail. The lion awoke and clapped his huge paw on the mouse and lifted it toward his huge mouth. "Please," begged the mouse. "Let me go, and I will always be grateful. One day I may be able to return the favor." The lion was so amused at the idea that a mouse could ever do anything for him that he dropped the mouse and let him escape. Later, hunters caught the lion in a trap and planned to deliver the King of Beasts alive to the prince of the land. They tied the lion to a tree while they went to get a wagon to carry him. The little mouse happened by and saw the danger the lion was in. The mouse gnawed through the ropes so the lion could escape. "See, I was right," said the mouse.

Moral of Aesop's Fable: Little friends may prove great friends

One afternoon, I am sitting in the exam room with Mr. Mann, a fifty-two-year-old patient, as we finish up his appointment for knee pain, which I have diagnosed as bursitis. I take a moment to review his preventive care history and suggest that he allow me to screen him for colon cancer due to his age.

"It is strongly recommended by experts—and by me—that everyone starts colon cancer screening at age fifty," I tell him.

He responds in a definitive tone, "Colon cancer does not run in my family."

Almost reflexively, I tell him about Mrs. Feller, anonymously, of course. She, too, declined my offers to do stool testing, I tell Mr. Mann. I had given her the kit twice, but she did not get around to doing it at home. I sat in the hospital many years ago, holding her hand and adjusting her morphine drip as she died of colon cancer.

"I hope I never have to do that again," I tell Mr. Mann wistfully at the end.

My goal in telling Mrs. Feller's story to Mr. Mann today is to take a recommendation which he may perceive as nothing more than an academic textbook item and bring it to a personal level in a nonthreatening way. In fact, I have used her story often. Only God knows if it has prevented another colon cancer death, but Mrs. Feller would have joined me today in hoping that it did. After we talk, Mr. Mann agrees to do the stool test.

Like Aesop's well-known fables, those cautionary tales that parents read to their children to teach valuable life lessons, I have a handful of patient stories that I retell. Aesop tells of the dog that looked into the lake and dropped the steak in his mouth to get a larger one from the other dog, which was actually just his own reflection. I tell of a young immigrant patient of mine who never received his baby shots and died of tetanus in the intensive care unit after many weeks of lying unconscious on a ventilator. There was a man with diabetes who did not check his feet regularly and came to me with a thumb-tack stuck in the ball of his foot. He did not feel it and had developed a raging infection.

These are my own fables. My goal, of course, is to allow my current patient to see a real-life adverse outcome of a former patient and hopefully to choose the healthier option.

Darrell is a thirty-two-year-old man who comes to see me today requesting to be checked for sexually transmitted infections. When I asked him for the reason, he tells me that he likes to get checked every year. Further questioning reveals no current infection symptoms, but he has had multiple female sexual partners in and around the local bars and never uses a condom.

"I don't like the way a rubber feels. I never use one."

"Now, that's just plain foolish," I tell him sternly. In the past, I was gentler in my wording, but in the past I had not diagnosed as much HIV disease and Hepatitis C. I delve into fable-mode.

"Last month I saw a man about your age," I begin slowly. As we talked that day, and I examined him, I began to suspect HIV disease. His only risk factor was that he was having unprotected intercourse with many women. After I got his blood tests back, I sat with him again, "in this very room, right where you and I are sitting now." I had to tell him that he was HIV positive.

Today, I admit to Darrell, "I am so tired of telling people who have had unprotected intercourse that they are HIV positive. HIV can become AIDS, which can be fatal." I bring our conversation to a more personal level. "Darrell, you are putting yourself at great risk by not using a condom."

I tell him that today we will collect blood and urine to screen him for STIs, but we will need to repeat the HIV blood test in six months.

Beads of sweat break out along his forehead. I see that he has not missed to moral of my own fable.

28

BEYOND THE ORDINARY

The patient stories that I remember with ease, as the years go by, are those that bookend the extremes of emotion: the exuberant victories and the tearful losses. These recollections represent the highs and lows of my medical practice and tend to be the ones I use to teach medical students. But there are hundreds, even thousands, of everyday experiences that far outnumber the memory-stickers. They are mundane, routine, even automatic, with pattern recognition playing a large part.

Here is a common pattern. An adult patient tells me that he has had right elbow pain for two weeks, a pain that is worse with using a heavy shovel. I examine his arm, probing the bony olecranon and lateral epicondyle, then palpating the soft tissue as I gently pronate and supinate his forearm with my other hand. In two minutes, I have diagnosed lateral epicondylitis: a minute and a half to listen to the man's symptoms, followed by a thirty-second examination. If it is a particularly busy day, I begin the examination of his arm as we are still talking. As soon as I recognize the familiar pattern on history and exam, I confidently announce to him the diagnosis. I prescribe naproxen, ice, rest, and a tennis elbow strap, as I have dozens of times in the past. Every time. I do not mull over the pathophysiology of overuse syndromes and tendon stress or the prostaglandin-fighting properties of nonsteroidal anti-inflammatory medications. And I almost certainly will not remember this one man's tennis elbow in a year's time.

But tucked inside such ordinary activities can be sublime moments if I am open to notice them and to receive their grace. I must remember that each elbow is connected to a person who has entrusted me not only with the health of their body but also their mind and spirit.

So, the patient with the sore elbow is actually a muscular black man, Darrell, who greets me with "Hi, Mom!" as I enter the exam room. As only he and I would know, he is referring to our last visit, when he told me that he never uses condoms because he did not like the way they feel. What ensued that day was my standard unprotected sexual intercourse spiel, which I have given dozens of times before. On that day, Darrell responded by telling me that I sounded like his mother, which we agreed was not necessarily a bad thing. He needed advice from someone who cared about him.

So, I get "Hi, Mom!" today, and my heart feels a bit happier. Just two short words—sublime.

Mr. Thompson, a middle-aged businessman, comes to see me for knee pain. He seems different today. Quieter? Sadder? I ask him if something is wrong, and he freezes. Sitting on the exam room table, he says nothing and I say nothing. I settle down into my chair, hoping that he feels my unspoken invitation to tell me anything he wants to. More silence. I notice the hum of the lights, and I am sure that he does not.

He looks at me with tired eyes and says tentatively, "I think ... I think that my son is on drugs."

From there flows his story, imbued with his sense of failure and helplessness. Our sitting without speaking has opened the door to his crushed spirit, and he reaches out to me for help. Just a moment of silence, then trust—sublime.

Juan is a six-year-old boy on the ward, whom I am treating with intravenous antibiotics and nebulizers for pneumonia. His mother has been frantic with worry and has not left the hospital in four days. During rounds this morning, I show her a much-improved chest x-ray. Her eyes meet mine, mother to mother, and the bliss of the moment flows between us and then settles placidly into our hearts. Just a chest x-ray—sublime.

When I was a resident, the pediatrics department held annual "birthday parties" for the babies who had been cared for in the newborn intensive care unit over the past year and were now at home, for the most part thriving. Some children were less than a year old, held in the protective arms of a parent. Many were toddlers running around the room as toddlers do. That morning, I re-connected with Amelia, a nine-month-old baby whom I had cared for after she was born. The mother and I recalled together the weeks of lines and tubes, the ultraviolet light treatment with the protective eyepatches, our reaching through the holes of the incubator to touch the baby's tiny hands. That day I held the baby girl in my arms, as I was never able to do in the ICU, and I looked at her sweet face. At that moment, her precious pink face was as grand to me as the frescoes of the Sistine chapel. Just chubby baby cheeks—sublime.

I spend a lot of time talking to my military veteran patients, asking about their experiences. Mr. Truesdale was in the Army, a "ground-pounder" in Vietnam. Since the 1970s, he has fashioned himself into an expert of sorts on the military action in Vietnam. In the course of our conversation I mention that my father was a FAC pilot.

"Forward Air Control," he says with excitement, "now *those* were the real heroes of the war. Their lives were on the line every second that they were in the air."

He proceeds to explain that these pilots—*my father*, I thought—flew O-1s, which were very small aircraft. Their mission was to fly low over enemy territory to identify targets in advance of the large bombers. The FAC pilots would drop white-phosphorus smoke bombs before "getting the hell outta there," as my patient put it. The planes were in the crosshairs of the Viet Cong surface antiaircraft weapons, and many of the pilots were killed.

After my father returned from Vietnam, he never told us about any of his combat experiences. Dad has been dead for a few years now, his story seemingly lost. As Mr. Truesdale speaks, I get goose bumps. Just a brief history lesson—sublime.

Ordinary events in my practice become *sublime* if I am careful not to feel rushed, if I am comfortable with silences, and if I focus on this exact moment and not the last or the next. These sublime moments have elements of awe, surprise, and exuberance, all wrapped up in the thought *I'm so glad I chose to be a family physician.*

29

TREASURE

"Near and dear to my heart," is how my mother described the tiny golden pilot wings and silver wedding band that dangled from a chain around her neck. My father died several years back, and after forty-nine years of marriage, she felt comforted by the tangible reminders of their union and his venerable career.

When I pay attention to seemingly insignificant things—what my patient is wearing around their neck, for example—a door is opened. Interesting conversations often ensue, and I gain important insights. I learn details about my patients that I may not have known otherwise: their relationships, their hobbies, their careers, even their spirituality. There is a very definite sense of intimacy and privilege that goes along with these mementos.

"May I listen to your heart and lungs?" is how it usually starts.

An elephant face made of rich brown ebony, with large golden ears off to the sides.

"Not many people can tell that it is an elephant!" laughs my patient, who then delights me with a story of his trip to Nairobi years ago.

A well-worn felt and ribbon scapular, known as a brown scapular by Catholics. My patient is obviously pleased that I recognized its meaning. We begin a conversation comparing area parishes, priests, and church activities, and an important common bond is revealed. She smiles when I tell her that this holy item was literally named for the anatomic scapular bone.

One of the most common neck chains is a cross, but even the variety in this simple symbol is astonishing. I see crosses of gold or silver, crosses made of two nails, crucifixes with intricate design, and those with stylistic simplicity, a cross shaped as an anchor. These are conversation starters, all.

From a patient who wears a golden cartouche spelling out her first name, we discover our mutual interest in Egyptology. No, neither of us had been to Egypt, but "perhaps someday," we dream.

"I see you still wear your military dog tags," I comment to another patient. He tells me in a hushed tone that they belonged to his brother, who was killed in Vietnam.

A large silver #3, which must be two inches tall, leads me to ask Mr. Garza what it means. After telling me that it was "Dale Earnhart's number," he becomes more animated in the exam room.

"Dale died in 2001," he tells me. But Mr. Garza still watches his auto races on TV, and in fact spends most of his day, every day, in front of his television watching racing. Here is a point of his social history that may have remained unknown to me had I not asked about his chain.

A thimble-sized gold cylinder hangs from a chain buried deep under Mrs. Sander's sweater. She pauses when I ask her about it and then explains that it contains the ashes of her dead son. Her voice is quiet, her words carefully chosen. He killed himself decades ago, after a breakup with his girlfriend. I thank her for the honor of hearing the story and ask her what her son was like.

Like a treasure map, our jewelry conversation can lead us to a deeply meaningful aspect of their life. Why else would they choose to wear *that* necklace, *that* symbol, under their clothing and close to their hearts, every single day? They are not wearing it to display to others, since it is often hidden. True, not all patients open up to me after I ask them about their necklace, but many do. That sharing is like a sparkling jewel, which I would not have found were it not for some digging.

30

INCHWORM

The next patient of the afternoon, Mrs. Lozano, new to my clinic, is coming in for allergy symptoms. My nurse reports to me that her blood pressure is in the borderline range today.

As I enter the exam room, she is sitting on the end of the exam table, wearing a flowery sundress. We smile at each other, and I introduce myself and ask how she is doing.

"Fine, doctor, but my allergies are really bothering me lately."

She goes on to tell me that she always reacts to the summer grasses of our area with itchy eyes and nose. Her story is punctuated with a few sneezes. We review her past medical history together, and I ask if she has any children.

"Funny you should ask me that. Today is the ten-year anniversary of my baby boy dying of SIDS."

For a moment, I am without words. A simple visit for allergies, which usually engages just the intellectual part of my brain, has been derailed by an emotional time bomb. I take a deep breath and put down my pen and pad, wondering to myself how comfortable she is with discussing this devastating event. Knowing that it is important to many parents that their lost child's memory be kept alive, I tell her how sorry I am and ask the briefest of questions.

"What was his name?"

"Steven," she responds, and after just a slight pause, she continues. "He was five months old when he died."

She goes on to tell me that she and her family still talk about Steven. From time to time she and her husband remind their two living children how much their brother had liked the train mobile above his crib.

"It's hard, though," she confides, "when people ask me now many children I have. I want to say three, because that is the true answer, but then I might need to explain about Steven dying. So, I usually say two and think to myself three."

"That must be hard. It sounds like you have a very close family."

The conversation is not over; it has just started. Mrs. Lozano tells me how she and her husband have been involved in the local SIDS support group, both here and in the city in which they lived previously. They talk with grieving parents, lending a sympathetic ear and providing help that only someone who has experienced SIDS firsthand can do. As she speaks, I feel privileged that she has chosen to tell me these intimate life experiences.

In a corner of my mind, a question creeps in. When during this fifteen-minute appointment is the right time to address her preventive care issues? She came to see me for her allergies, we are now discussing her baby's death, and yet there is still more to accomplish. Do I stop Mrs. Lozano mid-emotion and tell her that we must discuss instead her slightly elevated blood pressure and her smoking? These are the very items that my administrators and health insurance partners are measuring on a daily, weekly, and monthly basis.

Metrics, they are called—tidbits of data that can be measured, collected, aggregated, and put in colored charts. Such information is used to determine if Dr. Camosy is doing a quality job with her patients. Examples of metrics include:

1. the percentage of Dr. Camosy's patients with controlled blood pressure;

2. the percentage of Dr. Camosy's smoking patients who have been advised to quit;

3. the percentage of Dr. Camosy's female patients who are current on their mammograms and Pap smears;

4. the percentage of Dr. Camosy's diabetic patients who have had a monofilament foot exam in the past year;

5. the percentage of Dr. Camosy's depressed patients who have been screened for suicidal thoughts.

Camosy-Metrics I'd like to see will never come to pass, because they exist just in my mind, but I give them a high level of importance with my patients, nonetheless.

♥ the percentage of Dr. Camosy's sad patients who smiled;

♥ the percentage of Dr. Camosy's angry patients who were defused;

♥ the percentage of Dr. Camosy's fearful patients who were reassured;

♥ the percentage of Dr. Camosy's indigent patients who were provided with food and transportation assistance;

♥ the percentage of Dr. Camosy's lonely patients who felt listened to and cared about.

Sometimes I imagine that I can actually see women and men in business suits walking through the corridors of our hospitals, each carrying a yardstick in one hand and a clipboard in the other. I would have a song to sing for them, one that I learned in fourth grade:

> Inchworm, inchworm, measuring the marigolds...
>
> you and your arithmetic will probably go far.
>
> Inchworm, inchworm, measuring the marigolds...
>
> seems to me you'd stop and see how beautiful they are!

If you cannot sing this song with its melody, ask someone who is over fifty to do it for you. You will receive a musical treat right on the spot.

31

G IS FOR GOODBYE

Long one of my favorite patients, Mrs. Nguyen comes to see me one wintery afternoon for bronchitis. At the end of the visit, we walk down the clinic hallway together, lingering to make small talk and to plan her next visit date. She stops me with a gentle hand on my arm.

"Dr. Camosy, my mother-in-law is visiting from Vietnam. I wonder if you would check her blood pressure."

She explains that her husband, who came to America as a young man, flies his mother over to this country every year for a visit. The older Mrs. Nguyen enjoys visiting with her grandchildren, cooking Vietnamese food, and reminding them of their heritage.

"We eat a lot of spring rolls," my patient tells me with a grin.

When they come to the clinic a few days later, both the older and younger ladies greet me, one translating the Vietnamese for the other. My new patient is soft-spoken, nodding and smiling often. Her only medication is the blood pressure pill, which she forgot to bring from Vietnam. After I complete a medical history with her daughter-in-law's help, I ask her permission to listen to her heart and lungs and then complete my examination.

"Well, Mrs. Nguyen, I see that you are indeed a healthy woman," I tell her. "I will write out a prescription for you."

Her daughter-in-law translates, and the older woman nods. Our visit drawing to a close, Mrs. Nguyen the elder thanks me, and I see a real sense of gratitude in her smile.

"We are so glad to have you in the United States," I say, "and I hope your visit is a pleasant one. Please be sure to check your blood pressure at home every few days." Turning to her daughter-in-law, I ask, "How do you say *goodbye* in Vietnamese?"

"*Tam-byet!*" I manage to tell the elder lady in my best approximation of the pronunciation as they turn toward the clinic door.

Her smile broadens. A new connection has developed, and I am glad to be a doctor, to be *her* doctor. A few days later, her son brings to the clinic a platter of fresh, crispy spring rolls, just in time for lunch.

My office address book—the old-fashioned paper type, now decades old—is worn from use. Under 'G' is the word GOODBYE, which I wrote there in all caps many years ago. Logophilia, the love of words, is an inherited trait in my family, and thus I began learning the word *goodbye* in many languages. In my address book, I write the phonetic pronunciations of goodbyes from around the world to surprise my foreign patients at the end of their clinic visits.

So, today I write "Vietnamese—tam-byet" into my book, as I think again of Mrs. Nguyen and hope that she will do well. I recall that Mr. Feng seemed pleased when I bid him "*see gee in*" in his native Mandarin. Norwegian for Mrs. Nordland: "*hadet bra.*" A patient told me he was of gypsy origin, Serbian in particular. So, our farewell that day ended with him educating me by bidding me a "*do videnja!*" and a new entry made its way into my well-used address book.

Several "goodbyes" are not in my book. "*¡Adios!*" comes easily, and I can handle French, Italian, and German farewells by memory. But other languages elude me. Hence, the GOODBYE in my address book. Words are fun.

My father, who was of German origin, loved to explore languages, words, and grammar. He would routinely correct the news anchor people on TV, the journalists in the local newspaper, and his children. After I graduated from medical school, he loved to refer to me as "my Tochter, the Doktor," playing on the similar sound of the German words for *daughter* and *doctor*. This went on for years, decades even. He would sometimes follow-up with the question, "Pam, when are you going to stop practicing medicine, and do it for real?" I still chuckle when I remember his riffs.

Many of my patients prefer to speak Spanish, so over the years I have taught myself, with the distant memory of college Spanish class, how to speak medical Spanish. Because it is important for me to communicate with my patients the very best I can, speaking their language becomes a huge connection. I often joke that one cannot grow up in San Antonio without learning to love enchiladas and picking up Spanish.

It takes courage, though, to suspend the goal of perfection and to proceed with a conversation in Spanish without great proficiency. The first step is just to dive in. I started long ago by taking a Spanish translator into the examination room, but still conducting as much of the interview as possible myself in Spanish. I would ask the patient to help me with a word, with the triple goal of learning a new Spanish word, strengthening our personal interaction, and reinforcing the parity of our relationship.

With practice came proficiency, and now it is really fun to see the surprise on my patient's face when this *doctora gringa* greets them in Spanish and asks them "*¿Como esta usted hoy, señor?*"

For my hearing-impaired patients, I just wave to say "goodbye;" clearly, no address book entry is required. Night-school sign language classes have provided me with enough skill to partake in a basic medical conversation. I touch and twist slightly the tips of my two index fingers over any body part, my own of course, to ask if that area hurts. I find that I can sign better than I can understand responses, but my deaf patients do not mind at all.

Everyday words like "goodbye" may seem mundane, but when delivered with sincerity in their own language, they strengthen my relationships with my patients.

32

ON JUMPING RIGHT IN

For days now, the news has been telling us of the sound and the fury that Hurricane Katrina brought to the people of New Orleans. Visual images on my TV screen signify horrors that seem beyond belief. Homes, stores, hospitals, roads, and power lines are destroyed. Bridges crowded with now-homeless people seeking shelter and food seem about to collapse. A stadium filled with refugees is teeming in filth and chaos and even violence. Widespread looting of stores spreads, as the local police officers flee the inner-city section called the Fifth Ward.

Mother Nature brought utter devastation to millions of people in Louisiana, and now has touched us in San Antonio as well. We have been designated a refugee city, and very soon thousands of exhausted, hungry, and ill people arrive here by bus.

My sister, Margaret, a registered nurse, was among the first volunteers who were there at Kelly Building 171 to greet and care for the people who arrived that

Friday. She was exhausted afterward but called me that same evening to recount the events of her day. What she described was both dreadful in the scope of the human suffering and positive in the help that the volunteers were able to provide. These refugees from New Orleans, she told me, had endured stifling hot days wading in filthy water, then hours on un-air-conditioned buses. The odor of sweat, urine, and vomit escaped as the bus doors opened. She and her colleagues began the difficult task of attending to their most urgent medical and human needs—cleaning them, dressing wounds, giving them fresh clothes, and settling them in cots.

The next morning, moved by my telephone conversation with my sister, I grab my spare white lab coat from the hall closet. I tuck a few pens and prescription pads in one coat pocket, a stethoscope in the other, and head out with one of my daughters. As we drive, I wonder out loud what awaits us and think of the compassionate words of our San Antonio mayor, Phil Hardberger, on the national news just the night before:

"Whatever we are called upon to do ... we intend to welcome these people with open arms and to try to give them some dignity which these circumstances have taken away from them."

Now here is a mayor, I remark to my daughter, who embodies compassion and charity without concern for bureaucratic superfluities. Just do the right thing; we will figure out how we will pay for it later.

We arrive at the sprawling warehouse-style building on Kelly Base SA, and I am overcome by the sights and sounds and smells of the newly organized refugee center. Hundreds of exhausted people lie on rows and rows of cots, most resting quietly or sleeping. They are being tended to by dozens of Red Cross workers and volunteers. As we walk through the room and step around several cots, wafts of sweat and urine and baby spit-up swirl around us, underscoring the intense human needs still to be addressed. Groups of children color pictures with crayons, others are playing cards, and a teenager plays a guitar. Adults tend to babies in strollers, and I wonder how many babies lost their mommies, how many parents lost their babies.

A surreal sense of calm amid chaos strikes me, as my daughter and I smile at the people we see and squat down to talk to some of the children. Never before have I felt more a part of God's family; here are my brothers, my sisters, my children. Yes, we talk about it at home, and our priest preaches it on Sundays. As of today, my young daughter and I feel it in every fiber of our beings.

Hand-lettered paper signs taped to the walls lead us to our destination: "Medical →." The large room that has been designated to care for the medical needs of the refugees is divided into individual patient care areas by portable wall dividers. Volunteers are still setting up supplies in each area, today being the first full day of service. Toward the back of the room, a mini-pharmacy with basic medications is being carefully stocked. One other volunteer physician, an orthopedist, is in the medical area, as are several nurses. After I introduce myself and my daughter to the Red Cross person in charge of the area, she calls out to one of the nurses, "I have a doctor here for you to work with."

The nurse and I glance at the door marked "Patient Entry." The line of patients, young, old, and in between, winds down the hallway further than we can see, so we jump right in. My daughter heads to the boxes being unpacked, and I go sit in one of the cubby spaces, as the nurse brings me my first patient.

I wish I could say today that I remember their names. I do know that, on that day, I call each patient by name two or three times during each brief visit, as is my habit. Amid this throng of distressed people, in the lowest part of each of their lives, I want each one to feel cared for and cared about.

A middle-aged man, we shall call him Mr. Smith, shuffles into our area and sits down. His shirt and slacks are worn and dirty, but on his feet are new bedroom slippers. After our introductions, I ask him what he needs today.

He becomes agitated and tells me with staccato speech, "I need my insulin. I have not had it for three days now. I have never been off of it for so long!"

Further questioning reveals that he normally takes short-acting insulin before each meal, and that he now has frequent urination and blurred vision. A quick blood-sugar check reveals a value of 264, and the nurse and I breathe a sigh of relief that he will not need emergency care.

This same scenario plays out for me half a dozen more times that day. A surprising percentage of the refugees are insulin-dependent diabetics without their medications. Our supply cabinet contains a limited amount of rapid-acting insulin vials to administer for emergencies and, thanks to a donation from a pharmaceutical company, a larger supply of long-acting daily insulin. So, for Mr. Smith, a bit of mental math on my part allows me to convert him to a once daily insulin dose to correct his daily blood sugars for the time being. He will have to come here to the medical room each day for the injection, I explain to him, and I write the instructions on a piece of paper to help him remember.

While we are waiting for my nurse to get the insulin from the refrigerator, I ask him if his family is here with him. He tells me that he was separated from his wife and daughter during the chaos in New Orleans. He gave their names to the woman who checked him in when he stepped off the bus last evening, and he is praying to see them very soon.

I feel utterly hopeless and immensely sad for him, as I tell him, "I will pray for that, too."

We tend to people with fresh cuts, abrasions, and sprains. Some have respiratory trouble, some gastric symptoms. Two young pregnant ladies who are weak and dehydrated receive intravenous fluids.

Many of the patients that day have chronic medical conditions but do not have their pills; high blood pressure and diabetes take up much of our time. Using the limited supply of medications in the cabinet, I stave off a crisis for this group of refugee patients by lowering their blood pressure or blood sugar for a day or two. "Temporizing," we call it in the medical field; we dispense temporary supplies of medication and rely on the social workers on-site to help provide longer-term solutions. They are meeting with the refugees to enroll them in public benefits for medical care or to inform their private insurers of their new address at Kelly 171. The task seems herculean, but the workers and volunteers give it their all over the next few days, weeks, and months.

I return to volunteer several more times, and each session is both exhausting and energizing. One evening during the first week, I receive a call at home from a staffing agency, asking me to suggest any of my physician colleagues who might want to volunteer.

A few phone calls later, several of my friends agree to help. We now have a strong cadre of nurses and physicians who agree to give their time and talent to aid our newest San Antonio neighbors, the Katrina refugees.

Our Mayor Hardberger did not wait for funding before he opened our city to the refugees. I am glad, as well, that I did not wait to be asked to help on that Saturday, just the second day the refugees were here in San Antonio. The white coat and stethoscope that I grabbed that morning represent a dual blessing—one given to me by virtue of my medical degree and experience and another for me to give to others with a generous healing spirit.

33

CONCERTO

Allegro

Eager young faces of three medical students look to me as we sit around the table. I am now a seasoned physician, and we are talking about a favorite topic of mine: family medicine. Our annual residency fair is a sort of a speed-dating event, in which a new group of students joins me every twenty minutes all evening long. The goal in this rapid rotation is for me to assist them in the life-shaping decision of which medical specialty to choose.

"One reason I chose family medicine is its diversity," I tell each group of students.

Family physicians care for patients of all ages, with any symptom of any part of the body. Womb to tomb and top to bottom, I call it. I find this limitlessness exciting, I tell my listeners, hoping to transmit my enthusiasm to them this evening.

But there is more. Within this incredible breadth, I can also focus on topics and types of patients based on one of my own personal interests, music. Music centers my spirit and brings me back to my family roots.

"A house with music is a happy house!" I recall my mother saying. Making music is a very basic part of my identity, as is my desire to heal and to help.

Adagio

When my mother was on her deathbed, less than an hour before she died, my sisters and brother and I sang her favorite song for her. In *doloroso* three-part harmony, we intoned, "By the Rivers of Babylon ...," and the gift of music was returned to its very giver. Music is so powerful that it transcends time and even planes of existence.

My medical practice has seen an abundance of musicians over the years. Our mutual interest in music can be discovered in a number of ways—perhaps during our getting-to-know-you conversation in the clinic or by word of mouth through another patient or more directly with a music-related injury as the presenting complaint.

Mr. Romano is a delightful ninety-two-year-old man, Italian by birth with fine features and impeccable dress. He is cognitively intact but slowing in his daily activities. His first clinic visit a few months ago was for postherpetic neuralgia, a chronic nerve pain that can follow shingles. With effort, he climbed onto the exam table to show me where he was hurting: his left upper torso and shoulder. I noted that the inflammation of the vesicular shingles rash had evolved into a dark pigmentation that ran from the midline of his chest across his shoulder and back to the vertebral area on his back. His pain that day was intense; the mere weight of his shirt touching the skin caused discomfort. This despite his taking gabapentin every day to quiet the misbehaving neurons.

On that first visit, we chatted and got to know one another. He perked up when he told me that at one time he was a professional violinist, playing on stage with jazz groups across the country. He has a few musician friends left, but he had to stop "jamming" with them about half a year ago due to his painful shoulder. It was just impossible for him to hold his violin on his shoulder. He told me this with a wistful tone in his voice.

"But I have a CD of my music that I could bring you, Dr. Camosy, if you want to hear what I used to sound like!"

I changed his medications and advised him to begin heat and range-of-motion exercises on his shoulders, both of them. My goal was to relieve his pain and avoid a frozen shoulder.

Imagine my pleasure when he returns to the clinic to tell me that his pain is less severe and that he had picked up his violin again this week and started practicing scales and arpeggios, along with a few simple tunes.

"It feels so good to get back to my music. I feel young again!" he exclaims *con brio*.

That evening, I listen to his stringed jazz licks during my car ride home. My collection of recorded music from my patients continues to grow and give me pleasure. Mr. Romano's CD of violin music joins other CDs of original Christian vocal music and an old audiotape of modern self-composed vocal music. The names on the covers provide a glimpse of each artist: Be Still, From the Heart, Lake of Sky, Father's Day. Each is a reminder that my patients' lives intersect mine in extraordinary ways.

My patients have advised me how to better re-string my guitar and how to buy a sweet-sounding rainstick. They have invited me to hear them sing at their churches, and I have played piano for them at local nursing homes. How joyful is this two-part harmony between patient and physician.

Rondo

Connection to my patients through music is more than a shared avocation. Patients who have music-related illnesses and injuries present interesting challenges.

My patients appreciate being cared for by a physician who regards the Muse as seriously as they do.

A singer comes to my clinic, on a cold wintery morning, with bronchitis and laryngitis. She implores me that she just *has* to be able to sing for midnight Mass tomorrow. Oral medication and a steroid shot allow her to sing, to lift her praises to God.

Practicing overtime for a major concert caused a trombone player to come see me for pain in his moving wrist. I diagnose overuse tendonitis and provide him with a brace, relative rest, and an anti-inflammatory medication.

A mother wonders if her asthmatic daughter would be physically able to change from soprano recorder to the much larger bass recorder in the middle-school ensemble. The bass requires four times as much air to move through the instrument as the soprano, so we begin a program of increasing breath exercises and pulmonary training. These enable her to play the larger instrument, improve her lung capacity, and actually lessen her asthma symptoms.

A mysterious rash on his inner left knee brings a young man to my clinic. After several minutes of my questioning to find a physical cause, in true mystery-solving fashion, we hit upon the clue that he has just purchased a new cello. He has been practicing while wearing shorts. I cannot tell him why it affected just one leg, but hydrocortisone and wearing slacks cure the allergic dermatitis.

Coda

I drop a coin into the open guitar case of a musician at the street corner, and he nods back. Music is a powerful conduit: his chords touch me for a few seconds, my thanks sustains him, and he keeps his songs flowing for other busy travelers. This is how I view my care to my patients. The cascade effect makes the world a better place, person by person. The healing goes on and on, as does the beautiful music.

34

THE SANDWICH PEOPLE

I am preparing to see, Mrs. Preston, a widowed woman whom I have known for many years now. At eighty-two years old, she is still active and living at home, with the help of her adult children. I recall her being healthy overall, and a quick chart review reminds me that she has hypertension and just a touch of osteoarthritis. Her daughter called my receptionist just after lunch, asking if I would see her mother for a cough.

As I enter the exam room, I am reminded once again of why I enjoy family medicine. Two generations of patients sit before me. Here is a family of the older variety, each member living separately but forever connected to the other by bonds of love and time.

They greet me warmly, and the younger woman, Lois, tells me, "I know you are busy, Dr. Camosy, but I really wanted you to look at my mother before the weekend gets here. She has been coughing for a few days. Haven't you, Mom?"

Mrs. Preston nods, and answers the questions I pose to her to gather her history of present illness. Yes, she has been coughing for about a week, feeling tired and just a bit short of breath. No, she does not smoke and is not having chest pain, dizziness, or fever. I complete my physical examination and am fairly convinced that she has bronchitis.

"But let's get a chest x-ray to check for pneumonia, Mrs. Preston."

As we wait for her chest x-ray to be completed, I take a seat next to her daughter in the hallway.

"You know, doctor," Lois tells me, "I was at my daughter's poetry recital this morning when Mom called me. Justine really worked hard for two weeks to memorize her poem." She smiles. "She even added gestures and really made it funny."

She pulls a paper, folded neatly into quarters, out of her purse, and opens it for me.

"I think you'll enjoy it."

If I were ruler of the world

If I were ruler of the world
I'd make some changes fast
I'd say "the ruler's always first"
Her little brother's last

The ruler's older brother
Would have to listen, too
If I said "go eat a bug"
That's what he'd have to do

It goes on a few more verses, and I chuckle as I read it. Lois's eyes meet mine.

"I took the day off from work today for her poetry recital and made peanut butter cookies for the reception afterward. This was really a big deal for Justine. At least I was able to hear her recite her poem before I had to leave to bring Mom here. She was so cute; you should have seen her!"

Her voice becomes quieter and sad, and I lean in as she confides in me.

"Dr. Camosy, it was so hard for me to leave the school this morning to go pick up my mother. I felt so torn—my daughter or my mother. Who gets my attention right now? How can anyone make a decision like that?"

Lois goes on to describe how she and her siblings take their mother to her doctor appointments, pick up her medications at the pharmacy, and take turns helping her at home. At the same time, she and her husband have three young children. As she tells me this, her eyes well up, and I sense her frustration. Her heart and her time are being painfully tugged in two directions.

"I can see how difficult this is for you," I tell her, placing my hand over hers in her lap.

I explain that she is not the only one with this problem. Today's baby boomers are called the "sandwich generation," because our parents are living longer and often need assistance with health issues, home needs, and often finances. So we care for our aging parents while at the same time tending to the needs of our growing children. This sandwiches us in between the two generations.

Sometimes life runs smoothly, such as at family gatherings when everyone is together, celebrating their love and shared heritage. Food, laughter, and stories combine to create priceless memories for all.

Difficulties can be interjected, however, for the sandwiched person, as for Lois in my clinic today. The cumulative time and energy she spends on caregiving is doubled, and her personal relaxation time is halved. The most difficult situation, Lois and I agree, is when she feels as if a choice must be made in allotting the mere twenty-four hours in each day. She tells me that she feels as if someone is asking her, "Who do you love more?"

So, today I do my best, as the day is waning and we both are tired, to provide this loving daughter with words of understanding.

After I look at her mother's chest x-ray, I reassure both the patient and her daughter that there is no pneumonia. Mrs. Preston has a viral upper respiratory infection. I write a prescription for an expectorant and an inhaler to open her bronchial tubes. Equally important, I encourage Mrs. Preston to rest at home and to pay special attention to drinking lots of fluids.

A certain irony strikes me as I write the prescription. It is far easier to relieve my patient's respiratory infection than to lessen the stress of her sandwich-generation daughter. Medication will cure the bronchitis, but for Lois, a listening ear and a dose of emotional support is the best I can offer.

"To cure sometimes, to relieve often, to comfort always."

35

JIMINY CRICKET HAD IT RIGHT

Lawrence recently returned from a vacation in
Reno with stories of casino adventures and a discharge from his penis. He is a twenty-four-year-old
married patient of mine, who comes, ashamedly, into
the office to see me for the consequences of his sexual
indiscretion. After taking his history and confirming
the yellow discharge on physical examination, I collect specimens for sexually transmitted infections. I
treat him there in the office with intramuscular and
oral medications to cover gonorrhea and Chlamydia,
while we await the formal test results. We also discuss
the fact that I will be obligated to report the infection
to the state health department if the specimens return positive for any infection, and that I would also
treat his wife, because he had relations with her after
returning home. Lawrence is none too pleased about
this last part and asks me not to tell his wife. When I
tell him that she must be treated, he then asks me to

tell her that he does *not* have a sexually transmitted disease, but that I want to treat her as a precaution.

Mr. Ramsey was sick, too sick—he felt—to go to work. The problem is, he told his boss that he had come to my office to see me and that I had recommended that he not go to work that day. Later in the week, Mr. Ramsey asks me to write a sick note stating that I had seen him in my office to excuse him from work. He throws in, for sympathetic effect, that he will lose his job if I do not write the note for him.

Late one afternoon, I see Ms. Turner for a twisted ankle. When I get out my prescription pad to write her a naproxen prescription, she asks me if I would write another, also with her name, for her boyfriend, who does not have medical insurance. He has been sick with a cough and fever, and she feels he needs medication, but he cannot afford to come in to see me or to buy medication.

All three patients are asking me to be dishonest in some way: lie to the wife, fake a sick note, write a phony prescription. Most everyone, physician or not, has been placed in such a situation, asked to choose between the honest and dishonest paths. It is not as difficult as it may seem to say "no."

"My conscience will not allow me to do what you are asking. Would you like to discuss it with me?"

Generally, that settles the issue. Sometimes the patient persists, but I hold my ground and do what is right and honest. In the case of the woman who is asking me to write a prescription for her friend, I throw in the phrase "insurance fraud," which is a real conversation stopper.

In the movie story of Pinocchio, Jiminy Cricket twirls his umbrella and reminds the wooden puppet how important it is to tell the truth, with a song:

Take the straight and narrow path
And if you start to slide
Give a little whistle! Give a little whistle!
And always let your conscience be your guide.

A successful relationship between patient and physician requires mutual trust. Who would want to see a physician who is not honest? And how can I help a patient who is dishonest? After all, my therapeutic plan depends on the very facts that my patient tells me in their history. If they are not truthful, serious adverse outcome can ensue.

A patient assures me that she is taking her blood pressure medication faithfully every morning, and yet her pressure is high in my office. So I order a doubled dose of her pill, and we discuss this new plan while she is in the clinic. The next day, she calls my nurse to tell her that she had not been truthful—she often forgets to take the medication. I lower the dose back down and am thankful that no harm befell her.

A request for renewal of a narcotic pain medication crosses my desk. This patient is new to me, and the medical record indicates that he has been receiving 120 hydrocodone pills every month for quite some time. Yet, when I bring him in the following day for a urine drug screen, it is negative for opiates. A phone call to his home reveals that he is not taking the medication; his wife is. I cancel the prescription.

Every day, in large and small ways, every one of us must choose between the divergent paths of honesty and dishonesty. Within the intimate space of the patient-physician relationship, the decision can carry life-and-death implications.

36

ABRAZOS

Miss Reynolds is a waitress in her mid-thirties, on my morning clinic schedule today for a follow-up of her asthma. Her wheezing is under control with a daily preventive inhaler, and she expresses satisfaction with her current medications. Toward the end of our visit, she mentions offhandedly that she has a headache today. She is not asking me for help with this problem, which she says has been an almost daily occurrence since she was a teen. I get the definite impression that she is resigned to the pain.

"Tell me more about your headaches," I invite.

She describes a throbbing pain, today on the left but sometimes involving her whole head. She is matter-of-fact and not at all complaining.

"Would you like to schedule an appointment with me to discuss your headaches more?"

Surprise and happiness cover her face, and she agrees.

The following week, she returns to my office, and we delve right in. We talk about her pain, headache frequency, accompanying symptoms, and relieving factors. It becomes clear to me as we talk that she has common migraines combined with muscle tension headaches. I am the first doctor, she tells me, with whom she has discussed this in any real depth. She expresses frustration that these headaches have impacted her life as often and as severely as they have. She has suffered through twenty years of missed work, ruined vacations, and days spent at home in her darkened quiet bedroom.

Her first thought when she awakens each morning is, "Will this be a headache day or not?"

In my office today, I perform a neurological exam, and we go over my diagnosis. Together we make a plan: a night-time medication to try to prevent the headaches and another for her to take when the headache occurs. Keeping a headache diary is important, I tell her, to help us see any progress in an objective way. Before she leaves the clinic, I put my arms around her shoulders in a gentle *abrazo*, and tell her, "We are going to get you feeling better."

My patients tell me that my hugs are healing, so I deploy them often. Picture a patient with years of headaches that have never been explored, as with Miss Reynolds. Or think of a patient with any other undiagnosed long-standing symptom—abdominal pain, muscle pain, diarrhea, dizziness. The mere act of the physician listening, probing the details, and developing a plan of action becomes monumental in the life of that patient. The addition of the hug becomes therapeutic and puts real meaning to my intent and resolve. I want to her to know that I and my clinic team are on her side and that we will see her through to a solution.

I find myself hugging my patients frequently, usually as we are parting at the end of the clinic visit or hospital-room rounds.

A patient hospitalized for a stroke: "Here is a hug," I say, "for healing and strength to your arm."

A depressed patient in my clinic: "Here is a hug for peace and joy."

My hope is that our hugs, even wordless ones, will have a healing energy and will strengthen our physician-patient relationship.

Aliyah is a three-year-old wisp of a girl whom I am seeing at the free clinic. As I enter the exam room, she is leaning against her mother's legs, sucking on a yellow sippy-cup. Her sweet hazel eyes are taking in the room around her. I speak with her mother and learn of her daughter's symptoms—an earache and fever. Throughout our conversation, Aliyah watches me intently and inches toward me.

"How are you doing, sweetie?" I ask.

She offers me her sippy-cup, and I pretend to drink from it.

"M-m-m, that's tasty! How nice of you to share with me."

Her mother then tells more of their personal story. They are living in a transitional living facility for recently homeless families, and the mother is going to school to complete her GED. It is hard, she tells me, but she wants a better life for her three young children. We are sitting together now, our knees almost touching. I offer words of encouragement, mother to mother. It takes courage to make such bold changes and to do things she has never done before.

At the end of the visit, I give Aliyah a hug and tell her softly, "Thank you for being such a sweet girl!"

She embraces me enthusiastically.

We plan our next visit, and I put my arm around her mother's shoulders as we walk out of the exam room. "You are doing a great job raising your daughter. I can see she is friendly and smart, and look how polite she is. You are teaching her well!"

I sense that she needs to hear these comforting words. Mother and daughter walk down the hall hand-in-hand.

Aliyah turns back to tell me and calls out, "Tank-you, docta!"

My heart melts. Our hugs today represent multi-generational, multi-purpose therapeutic touch at its best. It just doesn't get any better than this.

37

TOO GOOD TO BE TRUE

Is there a medical test that is simple to perform, inexpensive, and curative as well? Yes, there is, and here is a clue: there is no technology involved.

Mr. Ybarra is an eighty-one-year-old man who has been my patient for many years. He comes to see me one day with his wife, complaining of weight loss. My chart review today indicates a very slow but definite fifteen-pound weight loss over the past year. As we talk, he tells me about his grandchildren who live far away in Seattle. One of them just became a lawyer, and the pride in his voice is evident. My symptom review is negative other than the weight loss. He has no nausea, vomiting, diarrhea, abdominal pain, and no signs of depression, no smoking, no alcohol abuse. His physical examination is reassuring, including his dentition. All in all, he looks hale.

His wife, who is more concerned about the weight loss than the patient is, asks me, "Do you need to do some blood tests, Dr. Camosy, or some x-rays?"

"Mrs. Ybarra, I would like to do something else first, something that will give me very valuable information. It is a test, of sorts, but very simple and absolutely risk-free for your husband."

Her eyebrows rise.

"It is a dietary diary. Mr. Ybarra, I would like you to keep a written food diary for me. That will allow me to answer a crucial question: Are you losing weight because you are not eating enough, or are you losing weight even though you are eating enough? Then I can decide how to best help you."

I hand him a two-page chart with blank boxes, for him to write down everything he eats and drinks for two weeks. Each page covers one week and is divided into breakfast, lunch, dinner, and snacks. I ask him to return in two weeks for a visit with my nurse, so she can collect the diary and re-weigh him.

Two weeks later, I review Mr. Ybarra's dietary diary, which reveals three healthy meals each day, interspersed with fairly healthy snacks. My nurse tells me that his weight is up two pounds. The couple told my nurse today that, prior to doing the diary, Mr. Ybarra and his wife had not noticed that he was eating less food every day and skipping meals. Once they paid attention to his food intake, his weight trended back up. We weigh him monthly for a few more months, and the weight he had lost returns. It was a simple problem with a simple solution.

Another all-too-common scenario in my office involves just the opposite. Ms. Taylor is forty-two years old and weighs 262 pounds. She comes to my office complaining of weight gain over the past few years, despite her assertion that "I eat like a bird." Her husband and three children keep her busy, as does her fulltime job as an executive. She is beginning to wonder if her being overweight is hampering her job effectiveness in terms of how her clients perceive her performance.

When she brings me her completed food diary two weeks later, listed is enough food to sustain a 400-pound ostrich. Her diet is rich in the less healthy "white foods"—bread, pasta, rice, and potatoes—and low in healthy vegetables and low-fat meat and fish. Plus, she nibbles high-salt snacks at her desk, almost unknowingly, as she works.

Ms. Taylor is genuinely surprised by the amount of food she eats, and the dietary diary proves helpful to her. After we talk for a while in my office, she agrees to a consultation with my favorite nutritionist. She begins to set her health as a priority and to make healthier choices. The dietary diary was the eye-opener in this case, an objective, low-cost tool to document for me and for the patient what is happening. The written record also serves as the starting point for the nutritionist's problem-solving.

After I discovered the salutary and sometimes curative effect of the dietary diary for patients who are losing or gaining weight, I found other creative uses of this low-tech, low-risk diagnostic "test." Think of any disease process whose treatment relies, even in part, on the patient making certain dietary choices; high cholesterol, diabetes, irritable bowel syndrome, and congestive heart disease are common examples. While it is easy for a physician to reach for a pre-scription pad or a lab requisition paper, the better choice may to take a mental step back and examine the patient's daily food choices more precisely.

For years, thirty-five-year old Mrs. Rayborn has repeatedly scheduled office visits with me for con-stipation. She has seen a gastroenterology specialist, who told her that she has benign chronic constipa-tion, without serious cause. At each visit, the patient assures me that she eats a high-fiber diet and drinks plenty of water, and I reassure her that there is no se-rious cause to be seen. I have given her my high-fiber diet handout. I have advised at least sixty-four ounces of water and a brisk walk every day. I have prescribed stool softeners with intermittent laxatives, all without success.

I began to dread seeing her name on my appoint-ment schedule, because each visit was the same: it seemed I could not help her.

Today when she comes to see me, the idea of using the dietary diary for her constipation pops into my mind. I give her my high-fiber diet paper again, along with the two-page blank dietary diary, and ask her to write down all she eats and drinks for the next two weeks, and to total up each day's fluid and fiber intake. I ask her to document her exercise as well.

Months pass, and I do not see Mrs. Rayborn's name on my clinic schedule. I actually forget about her and her constipation until she comes in for a well-woman appointment. When I ask her about her constipation, she tells me that it is about the same.

She admits, however, "I realized that I should not complain to you if I am not following your recommendations."

Even though research studies have shown limitations to the accuracy of the self-reported dietary diary, I have discovered it to be a valuable tool to assess my patient's nutrition in my clinical practice. I trust my patients to complete it more or less truthfully. Most of my patients genuinely want to be healthier and feel better and will be honest in the diary entries.

This is the age of technology, of more precise and faster diagnosis: blood tests, imaging, even screening scanners in church parking lots. Couple these advances with the time crunch that all physicians are under in their clinics, and one can easily see how much easier it is to order a series of lab tests (*check, check, check* in the requisition boxes) than to actually sit and talk with the patient for ten minutes.

Still, the "history of present illness" remains the most important part of physician decision-making, even more important than the physical examination or any blood work or imaging tests. I view the dietary diary is an extension of the history and an excellent way to see what choices my patient is making in their day-to-day life.

The dietary diary as a diagnostic tool is not too good to be true; it is true.

38

AT YOUR SERVICE

Mr. Santiago had surgery on his right elbow last week, and his arm is in a sling. We sit together in my clinic, talking about his surgery and his family. His grown daughter has come from Oklahoma for a few weeks to help him recuperate, since he is a widower and all alone in his trailer home.

His appointment today is a follow-up of his diabetes and hypertension. After listening to his heart and lungs, I ask him if I could examine his feet, and he nods. As I bend over to untie his shoes for him, he stops me with his healthy arm.

"Dr. Camosy, you don't have to do that! I will do it."

I glance at his immobilized arm. "It's my pleasure and no trouble at all."

Gently removing his shoes and socks, with his limited assistance, I note that they are quite worn. I perform a vascular and neurological examination and then help him replace his socks and shoes, tying the laces for him. We discuss diabetic foot care, and I remind him that his insurance will pay for a new pair of diabetic shoes and socks every six months. He takes me up on the offer to order these for him.

While getting up from the chair to leave, Mr. Santiago thanks me profusely for helping him take his shoes off and put them back on, telling me, "Your nurse could have done that."

A while back, Mrs. Underwood came to see me after suffering a deep wet cough for a week. She was elderly and very sweet, with severe spinal stenosis which had led to her needing a wheelchair to get around outside of her house. When I entered the room, she was sitting on the exam table, looking tiny and frail, her arthritic fingers resting in her lap. My nurse had placed her there and helped her take her blouse off so that she could don a paper gown. Mrs. Underwood and I spoke for a while, and she told me she had a cold that would not go away. I examined her thoroughly, and we both were relieved that I did not find anything more serious than a viral upper respiratory infection, doctor-speak for "a cold." Rest and fluids should help her feel better, and we made plans for me to re-check her in a week if there was no improvement.

Together we put her blouse back on, and I asked her if I could button it for her. She nodded. I helped her down into her wheelchair.

After I wheeled her through the hallway and back to the waiting room, she told me in amazement, "Dr. Camosy, this is the first time a doctor has ever done all this for me!"

Even when I am busy in my clinic, and really *really* need to move on to my next patient, I find that a simple act such as helping the patient with his shoes and socks, her shirt, his knee brace, is full of value for both me and my patient. The action is meaningful in terms of serving my patient at the most basic level, meaningful in terms of strengthening the physician-patient bond, and meaningful in terms of Pope Francis's reminder that it is the right thing to do.

I read in the daily paper:

ROME (Associated Press) 2013— Pope Francis washed and kissed the feet of a dozen inmates at a juvenile detention center in a Holy Thursday ritual that he celebrated for years as archbishop and is continuing now that he is pope... the Vatican released a limited video of the ritual, showing Francis washing black feet, white feet, male feet, female feet and even a foot with tattoos. "This is a symbol, it is a sign—washing your feet means I am at your service," Francis told the youngsters.

In our practices, we physicians are given the opportunity to cross an invisible line. We cannot see this line unless we are looking for it, and many never even find it. It is the line that separates the complex patient care that we have been trained for from patient service that honors basic personhood.

In crossing this line, we actually erase it.

Linger in the exam room just a second or two longer in gentle silence. Help a hospitalized patient onto a bedpan. Raise the head of the bed for her. Button the shirt of an elderly arthritic patient. Such acts of caring were not mentioned in my medical school classes. But that is the very point. The world is changed by simple acts of kindness, acts that remind both giver and receiver that no one person is more important than any another.

39

"TO THINE OWN SELF BE TRUE"

Black spiky hair, neck tattoos on her thin frame, and a patina of disinterest: all contribute to Lucy's tough persona. She is a sixteen-year-old girl who was legally emancipated from her parents because she is living on her own and supporting herself with a secretarial job at a nursing home. It has been hard for me to get to know her, even after three visits to my clinic. Even so, she has always been polite, and I detect that she is beginning to trust me.

She comes to my office today complaining of a purulent vaginal discharge. With a few questions, I discover that she had been sexually active with several boys, all without protection. A few months ago, she suffered painful blister-like lesions in her labial area, which resolved on their own.

At the visit today, I do a pelvic examination and collect blood, vaginal, and cervical samples for sexually transmitted infections. After she gets re-dressed, I motion for her to move from the exam table to the chair across from me. I tell her that I want to treat her today with antibiotics to cover for gonorrhea and Chlamydia.

Her facial expression does not change, as she mumbles, "Whatever."

"I also believe, Lucy, that you had genital Herpes recently, from what you told me about those painful blisters. I would like to do some blood tests for Herpes and also syphilis, HIV, and Hepatitis C. Is that alright with you?"

She nods.

It is time for a heart-to-heart talk. I ask her about the boys she knows, those she has sex with, and why she has sex with them.

"It's just for fun—it doesn't mean anything," she tells me. Then, vulnerability creeps into her voice as she tells me that all the boys she goes out with expect it of her.

"I am a bit different than most doctors," I tell her, trying my best not to sound like a parent admonishing a child. "I recommend that my single patients, female and male, not be sexually active." I pause for just a second, and say a silent prayer for us both. "I care about you, Lucy, and want you to be safe. Having sex with many young men, as you are doing, is dangerous. It can lead to pregnancy and cause diseases that are very serious—the ones I just told you about."

This is the talk that I have had with many patients, and sometimes it starts to feel like a lecture. But today I feel compelled to go on with one more important point, wishing that we had an hour more to talk. I know that Lucy has no healthy parental influence in her life.

"Lucy, some of my single patients who are sexually active have decided to stop. They thought that once they lost their virginity, they had no choice but to keep having sex, that it 'did not matter,' as you just told me. But it can be a healthy experience to stop being sexually active for a while."

She actually seems interested in what I am saying.

"Plus, it will free you up to think about *you*, to focus on what is best for your life. What do you think of when you think about your future?"

She mentions beautician school and perhaps having an apartment of her own. Her eyes soften as we talk more, and I feel honored that she has finally opened up with me.

As I matured in my medical career, I discovered that my early mentors who told me that I must keep my own opinions and moral viewpoints to myself when treating patients were dreadfully wrong. It may be politically correct to accept behavior of any kind without raising an eyebrow, but in many cases the guidance of a caring physician can be more healthful.

The preface to appropriately expressing my opinions is to let my patients know that I genuinely care about them and to remain open to conversation and the exchange of ideas. And if, during our discussion, my single patient decides to continue to be sexually active, we discuss condoms and contraception. At least they have been exposed to alternative—and more healthful—behaviors. At the end of the day, I must feel comfortable with my decisions about patient discussions.

Thinking again of Lucy, would I be comfortable just treating her multiple sexual infections without telling her that I recommend she abstain from sexual activity? After all, earlier today, I advised half a dozen smokers that they should stop *their* risky behavior.

Each physician possesses moral anchors that guide the care of their patients. We must listen compassionately to our patients and tell them often that we care about them. As Shakespeare reminds us in Hamlet, "This above all, to thine own self be true."

40

HEART TO HEART

Oh, dear God, I thought, *I am going to have to tell his children that their daddy has died—that I could not save him.*

Pushing aside the negative thoughts, I continue rhythmically compressing the center of his chest as he lies on the hard floor. His wife, thank God, knows CPR, and is breathing into his mouth after every thirty compressions. She is sweating and terrified, yet perfectly up to the task. Compressions—breaths—compressions—breaths. I count aloud to keep our rhythm going.

Just ten minutes earlier I was in my kitchen pouring Cheerios into bowls and orange juice into glasses. My daughters and I were immersed in our school-day routine, chatting happily about yesterday's playground hoopla and today's spelling test.

A frantic knock on the kitchen door ended the calm. I opened the door and saw our two neighbor girls, breathless and wide-eyed.

"Mommy says come quick. It's Daddy."

One girl pulled my hand, and I followed, wearing my bathrobe and pink fuzzy slippers, my hair in curlers. We ran across the dewy grass, through the open front door, up a flight of carpeted stairs, and straight into the bathroom.

Linda told me in a quivering voice that she found him slumped over the sink, motionless and unresponsive. She had eased him down to the tile floor where he now lay on his back, his skin pale, lips a sickening shade of blue.

"I just called 9-1-1," she said.

As I knelt onto the tile next to Daniel, my actions flowed from experience. ABC. Assess his airway and position his head and neck to open the air passage. Was he breathing? No, he was not. Circulation? No carotid neck pulses. The ABC assessment took less than ten seconds, and I began rescue breaths and chest compressions. Fingers intertwined and arms straight, I pumped up and down briskly and forcefully. I asked Linda to continue the breaths, blowing air into his lungs and watching for his chest to rise.

As she and I settle into a grim nonstop pattern of compressions and breaths, there is no sign of recovery from Daniel, no sign of life. Still pumping, I take a deep breath myself, looking around the room for a moment.

We are alone, a doctor, a patient, and his wife—or, just as correctly, three friends, one on the verge of death. I hear my own daughters downstairs playing with my friends' young children and then the distant sound of a siren.

Linda and I pray out loud together, "Dear Lord, please bring your life to Daniel."

But my own thoughts at the moment are pessimistic. I have done CPR scores of times over two dozen years as a physician. I have taught it to rooms full of doctors and nurses, and we all knew that the likely outcome for a patient who "codes" at home is not a favorable one. Today, though, my patient is my longtime friend—my neighbor, my fellow school parent, a member of our church. All Linda and I can do now is keep pumping, blowing, and praying, as the sound of the siren grows louder.

Three uniformed EMTs bound into the bathroom, laden with equipment. I move back as one EMT kneels by my side to take over chest compressions, and another positions himself near Daniel's head. I fill them in on what has happened in the last few minutes that seemed like hours. My hair curlers, I now realize, have tumbled down, half in and half out of my hair, and I resist the urge to feel self-conscious in my blue velour robe and pink slippers.

An EMT applies the defibrillator paddles to Daniel's chest within a minute of their arrival —"ALL

CLEAR"—and shocks his heart. Within seconds, the heart tissue begins its automatic contractions again. My friend is back among the living, among those who love him so dearly. He begins to breathe on his own and to move around, and then his eyes flutter open. An oxygen mask is placed on his face, dialed up to full flow.

Leaning down to floor-level once again, I tell him, "Daniel, it's Pam."

His eyes turn to meet mine.

"You are going to be fine. Your heart gave you some trouble, but it is better now. Can you hear me?"

He nods ever so slightly then looks over at his wife, who squeezes his hand.

At that point, I recall something he told me years ago. His older brother had died suddenly when he was alone at work. His heart had stopped. Chills course through my body.

As the stretcher is brought up the stairs, I walk out of the bathroom to make more room for the EMTs. Walking down the stairs, my legs are stiff from kneeling on the hard tile, my arms are aching, but my heart is soaring with joy.

Expecting to see his daughters and mine, the sight before me as I descend to the living room is astounding. Every inch of the room is filled with caring, worried neighbors, including our small-town mayor and police chief. Now I do feel self-conscious and quickly pull the drooping curlers out of my hair and stuff them into the pocket of my bathrobe.

I bend down to tell the girls that their daddy is doing better and that he will be going to the hospital to help his heart to heal. There are hugs all around, a prayer together for Daddy, then more hugs.

Daniel has thanked me many times for my care that day.

"You only live twice!" he quips, and we both know that how true that is for him.

Each May on the anniversary of the day, I receive a card and flowers from Daniel, who has fully recovered and now has an implanted defibrillator. Each note includes a running total of how many days he has been alive since that fateful day.

> Ten years of Life. I cannot thank you enough for giving me the extra time with my wife and daughters and Life in general. Thank you with all my heart. 3652 days. It's good to be alive.

It *is* good to be alive, dear reader. Keep the joy. Heal one another.

END NOTES

Chapter 3 – "Desiderata," poem by Max Ehrmann, published 1927

Chapter 9 – Mother Teresa quote, http://www.catholicapostolatecenter.org/blog/ small-things-with-great-love, accessed June 25, 2016

Chapter 12 – "diminishes me" from the poem "No Man is an Island" by John Donne, published 1624

Chapter 14 – "American Diamond 1969," poem by Pamela Camosy, 2014

Chapter 20 – Eeyore quotes, http://www.winnie-pooh.org/eeyore-quotes.htm, accessed April 13, 2014

Chapter 30 – "Inchworm," song by Frank Loesser for the 1952 movie *Hans Christian Anderson*

Chapter 34 – "If I were ruler of the world," poem by Bill Dodds, published 2005; aphorism by Dr. Edward Trudeau, 1800s

Chapter 35 – "Give a Little Whistle," song by Leigh Harline and Ned Washington for the 1940 movie *Pinocchio*

DISCUSSION QUESTIONS

1. In her introduction, the author stated that "hospital systems, health insurance companies, and the federal government have wrested control of medical practice from individual physicians." How has the author dealt with this change? How has it affected you personally?

2. Can you recall a time when you, as a patient, felt that your physician truly cared about you? What did they do or say to give you this impression?

3. Conversely, can you recall a time when your physician seemed not to care about you as a person? What did they do or say to give you this impression?

4. In several chapters, the author used stories from her early life to frame her adult patient interactions. What childhood experiences and relationships in your life have informed your own adult attitudes?

5. Bioethicists refer to the four basic principles of ethical healthcare: autonomy, justice, beneficence, and non-maleficence. Read the definitions of these terms at the University of Washington School of Medicine website, https://depts.washington.edu/bioethx/tools/princpl.html. Then find corresponding examples of each principle within four patient stories in *Healer's Heart*. How does the author make use of the principle in each case?

6. Find at least three instances in the book in which the author became the person who was helped or healed. Then, recalling the story about the kind Russian salesclerk, can you remember a time when a stranger provided healing for you? What interpersonal theme do these situations reveal?

7. This book took you inside the mind of a physician as she cared for her patients. In "Doin' Jes Fine," she described wanting to get away from her patient, and in "Broken," she decided to fire her patient. Were you surprised by any of her thoughts or motivations? Why or why not?

8. Dealing with poverty on a personal level was a theme throughout the book. What are some ways

that any person, medical or nonmedical, can address this societal problem?

9. What may have been some of the reasons that Tootie donated her body to science? Do you share these motivations?

10. After reading the chapter "Snapshot," did you gain insight or understanding that may impact your interactions with military veterans? If so, describe.

11. In "The Sandwich People," the author quoted the centuries-old healer's adage: "To cure sometimes, to relieve often, to comfort always." What does this mean to you?

12. One of the author's patients contemplated suicide. What was her response as a physician? In what ways might each of us help a depressed or suicidal person in a nonclinical setting?

13. In "Violation," the author cared for a patient who had been sexually assaulted. Afterward, she "feels a sudden need to…squeeze out my emotional sponge." Why do you suppose that she decided instead that

"perhaps I should not try to rid myself of the discom-fiture..."?

14. Rather than presenting a chronological narrative of her medical career, the author chose to describe interactions with specific patients. How does this choice help or hinder the presentation of the overall theme of healing?

15. Which patient story did you find most thought-provoking? The most surprising? Why?

16. What impressions do you think the author hoped that her readers would take away from their reading experience?

ABOUT THE AUTHOR

Pamela Camosy is a practicing family physician and writer in San Antonio, Texas.

After growing up in a military family and traveling across the world, she attended the University of Texas at Austin, where she received a BA in biology in 1976. She completed medical school at the University of Texas Health Science Center at San Antonio (UTHSCSA) in 1980 as a US Navy scholarship student. She spent eight years as an active duty Naval physician from 1980 to 1988 and has been in civilian practice since then. In 1993, she and her family returned to San Antonio.

In addition to her medical practice, she has served since 2004 as an adjunct Assistant Professor in the Department of Family and Community Medicine at UTHSCSA. In this role, she teaches medical students in her office, in lectures and grand rounds, in free clinics, and at health fairs. Her passion is remaining joyful and creative in her profession and encouraging everyone she meets to do the same.

She has been a writer since childhood. As an adult, she has published scholarly articles in *American Family Physician* and *The Journal of Family Practice* and serves as manuscript reviewer for these journals. In the 1980s, she wrote a regular bioethics column for the *New Catholic Miscellany*, South Carolina's official Catholic newspaper. In 2014, she felt called to return to creative writing pursuits and has since had poetry and prose published in San Antonio. *Healer's Heart: A Family Physician's Stories of the Heart and Art of Medicine*, stories of her patients that focus on the healing power of the physician-patient relationship, is her first book-length work.